漫画中国思想系列

Chinese Thought Comic Series

仁者的叮咛　兵学的先知

CONFUCIUS SPEAKS · SUNZI SPEAKS

The Messaje of the Benevolent
The Art of War

孔子说·孙子说

蔡志忠 / 编绘

[美] 布莱恩·布雅 / 译

中国出版集团

现代出版社

图字：01-2005-0833

图书在版编目（CIP）数据

孔子说·孙子说 / 蔡志忠编绘；（美）布雅
(Bruya, B.) 译 . -- 北京：现代出版社, 2013.8
（蔡志忠漫画中国传统文化经典：中英文对照版）
ISBN 978-7-5143-1664-3

Ⅰ．①孔… Ⅱ．①蔡… ②布… Ⅲ．①漫画－连环画
－作品集－中国－现代 Ⅳ．① J228.2

中国版本图书馆 CIP 数据核字（2013）第 183072 号

蔡志忠漫画中国传统文化经典：中英文对照版

孔子说·孙子说

作　　者	蔡志忠　编绘
	［美］布莱恩·布雅（BRIAN BRUYA）译
责任编辑	袁　涛　崔晓燕
出版发行	现代出版社
地　　址	北京市安定门外安华里 504 号
邮政编码	100011
电　　话	010-64267325　010-64245264（兼传真）
网　　址	www.1980xd.com
电子信箱	xiandai@cnpitc.com.cn
印　　刷	北京诚信伟业印刷有限公司
开　　本	710×1000　1 / 16
印　　张	19
版　　次	2013 年 10 月第 1 版　2013 年 10 月第 1 次印刷
书　　号	ISBN 978-7-5143-1664-3
定　　价	32.80 元

目录
contents

孔子的一生
The Life of Confucius

孔子的一生
The Life of Confucius

周灵王二十一年，公元前五五一年，孔子生于鲁国昌平乡陬邑。

Confucius was born in the town of Zou, Changping county, in the state of Lu in the 21st year of the Zhou King Ling (551 BC), during China's Spring & Autumn Period of the Zhou dynasty.

燕

齐

鲁

孔子的父亲名叫孔叔梁纥，身长十尺，武力绝伦，元配生九个女儿，妾虽生一个儿子，可惜是残障儿。

Confucius' father was Kong He, who stood six feet eight inches tall and was unsurpasse din strength. After his first wife had given birth to nine daughters, the elder Kong hoped desperately for a son, and although the next child born was male, he turned out to be crippled.

于是孔子的父亲在六十四岁以后，又娶了颜氏，才生了孔子。

So at sixty-four years old, Kong He took a young woman of the surname Yan as his second wife, and she gave birth to Kong Qiu, known to later Chinese as Kongfuzi, Master Kong, Latinized as Confucius.

孔子三岁的时候，父亲就死了。

When Confucius was only three years old, his father passed away.

孔子小的时候游戏，常摆弄各种祭器……

When Confucius was a child, he played games in which he arranged ritual vessels...

喜欢模仿大人祭祀时的礼仪动作。

And imitated the ceremonial gestures of adults.

孔子十五岁就立志向学。
At fifteen, he set his mind on learning.

十九岁时，娶宋之并官氏。
At nineteen, he married a woman from Song of the surname Bingguan.

第二年生了一个儿子，取名叫孔鲤。
The following year, he had a son, whom he named Kong Li.

孔子二十岁曾做仓库管理员，
At twenty years-old, Confucius worked as a manager of a granary,

出纳钱粮，他算量得准确清楚。
He figured the accounts with great accuracy and clarity.

孔子也担任过管理牧场的小职务，将场中牲口养得很好，越养越多。
He also held a minor managerial position at a ranch. And under his supervision, the number of animals steadily increased.

后来他又出任主管营建的司空。
Later, he assumed the office of minister of public works.

鲁昭公二十年，南宫敬叔推荐孔子到周去学礼。
In the twentieth year of Duke Zhao of Lu, Nangong Jingshu recommended that Confucius be sent to Zhou to study the ceremonies.

在周学礼时，孔子曾去拜见老子，向他问礼。
While studying the ceremonies in Zhou, Confucius paid a visit to Laozi to ask him about the ceremonies.

学成告别时，老子送他说：
After their session, Laozi sent him off with these words:

富贵的人送人用财物，仁德的人送人用言辞，我不是富人，就送你几句话吧。
The wealthy send people off with gifts, and the benevolent send people off with words. Since I am not wealthy, I give you these words:

聪明的人常遭困厄，是因他喜欢议论别人；学问渊博的人常遭危险，是因他好揭人罪恶；做人子女的应心存父母，做人臣属的应心存君上，不能只顾自己。
Intelligent people often encounter trouble because they tend to criticize others. Learned people often encounter danger because they tend to expose the misdeeds of others. Children should be mindful of their parents, and subordinates should be mindful of their superiors. Don't always think only of yourself.

孔子从周回鲁之后，门下的学生就愈来愈多了。
After returning to Lu from Zhou, Confucius' disciples began to increase at a steady rate.

这时齐景公带晏婴来到鲁国……
It was at this time that Duke Jing of the state of Qi and his chief minister, Yan Ying, paid a visit to Lu...

孔子，我向你请教一个问题。
Confucius, I'd like to ask you a question:

从前秦穆公国家小，地处又偏僻，他为什么能够称霸？
Duke Mu of Qin had a small out-of-the-way country, and yet he was later recognized by all as overlord of the land. Why was this?

秦国虽小，目标却很远大；地位虽偏，施政却很正当。亲自举拔用五张黑羊皮赎来的贤士百里奚，把政权交给他。
Although his country was small, he had expansive ambitions. Although his country was out-of-the-way, his government was just. He hand-picked the great administrator, Baili Xi, purchased him for five black sheep skins, and handed over governing authority to him.

从这些事实来看，就是统治整个天下他也能办得到。
From these facts, you can see that he was capable of reigning over the whole land.

称霸诸侯还算成就小呢！
To be recognized by the nobles as their overlord was but a minor accomplishment for him.

分析得很好！
Analyzed wonderfully!

孔子三十五岁的时候，鲁国的三个大夫联合围攻鲁昭公，昭公兵败逃到了齐国。
When Confucius was thirty-five years old, the three most powerful Lu noblemen united in an attack against their own Duke Zhao. When defeat was immanent, Duke Zhao escaped to the neighboring Qi state.

孔子想借齐国大臣高昭子的关系接近齐景公，于是做昭子的家臣。
In the hopes of getting close to Qi's Duke Jing through a high minister named Gao Zhaozi, Confucius accepted a position as household minister with Gao.

不久，鲁国又发生乱事，孔子也来到齐国。
Not long after, disorder again erupted in Lu, so Confucius also found his way to Qi.

孔子在齐国听了韶乐，一连学了三个月，吃饭连肉味都觉不出了。
It was at this time that Confucius was first exposed to the famous Shao Music created long before by the ancient sage Shun. Confucius was so impressed by the music that he studied it continuously for three months, and he was so enamored of it that even the taste of meat escaped his notice.

Bong

真没想到学音乐会使人到这个境界啊！
I never knew the study of music could bring one to such a state!

春秋时政治很乱，君不君，臣不臣，鲁昭公被大夫季孙氏所逐。
The Spring & Autumn Period in China was a frightfully chaotic time, with kings and ministers failing to play their appropriate roles. Duke Zhao of Lu ended up being toppled and exiled by the nobleman Jisun.

齐景公又受控制于陈桓，陈桓的势力很强大，大有篡夺政权的可能。
And Duke Jing of Qi was the puppet of one Chen Huan. As Chen Huan's power grew, the chances of his completely usurping the throne grew as well.

因此，齐景公问孔子为政的道理时，孔子说：
So Duke Jing sought advice from Confucius on the principles of governing. Confucius replied:

国君要像国君，臣子要像臣子，父亲要像父亲，儿子要像儿子。
Kings should act like kings; ministers should act like ministers; fathers should act like fathers; and sons should act like sons.

对极了，如果君不君、臣不臣、父不父、子不子，那么有再多的粮食，我们能平安地吃到吗？
Excellent! If people don't play their appropriate roles, then no matter how much food there is, will we ever be able to eat it in peace?

为政的原则又怎样？
What's another principle of governing?

为政最重要的是在善用财力，杜绝浪费。
The most important thing in governing is to utilize revenue intelligently and avoid waste.

我想把尼溪的田封给孔子。
I think I'll enfeoff Confucius with the Nixi fields.

儒者都能言善道，态度高傲，是很难驾驭的。他们不事生产，只是到处游说求职来进行政治活动。

These sophists talk a good talk, sire, but they're proud and difficult to control. They're also completely unproductive. All they do is travel around selling their ideas, hoping to get a good position and implement their own reforms.

这种人不能来掌理国事。

Don't let them get control of the government.

好吧! 就不用他罢了。

All right, all right. We'll just forget him.

这时，齐国的大夫有人想害孔子。

Meanwhile, some high level officials of Qi were also plotting against Confucius.

我老啦，没法用你了。

I'm getting old and so will have no further use for you.

景公也告诉孔子说：

Duke Jing said to Confucius:

老师，听说有人想要陷害您啊!

Master, I've learned that there are people who wish to do you harm!

哦! 是吗……

Oh! Is that right...

是吗……

Is that right...

于是孔子就离开齐国，回到鲁国。

So Confucius left Qi and returned to Lu.

鲁昭公被逼出国，流浪了七年，终于死在国外，于是鲁定公即位。
Duke Zhao of Lu had lived in exile for seven years and finally died outside his country. Duke Ding succeeded him.

定公仍毫无政治权力，一切都受到季孙氏、叔孙氏、孟孙氏三位大夫摆布。
But Duke Ding had yet to accumulate power and so was controlled by the powerful noblemen, who were all descendants of the long-ago Duke Huan. Because of this lineage, they were known in short as the Three Huans.

而掌握鲁国大权的季孙氏又被他的家臣阳货挟制得束手无策。
The majority of power in Lu was held by Jisun Yiru, but he himself was intimidated by his own household minister, Yang Huo.

鲁定公五年，阳货发动政变，代替了季桓子的地位。
In the fifth year of Duke Ding's reign, Yang Huo staged a coup and took the place of Jisun.

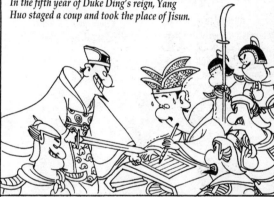

更挟持鲁君，放逐敌党，成了鲁国的独裁者。
Having even more control of the duke now, he exiled his enemies and effectively became the tyrant of Lu.

孔子不愿出任不守礼分的政权的官职，于是闲退在家，专心研究诗、书、礼、乐。
Unwilling to serve this illegitimate government, Confucius retired to his home and concentrated his efforts on researching the classic books of poetry, history, ceremony, and music.

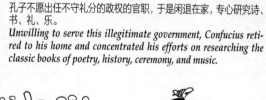

阳货也晓得延揽人才，想拉拢孔子，但孔子不想见他。
Understanding the importance of having able-bodied ministers, Yang Huo attempted to entice Confucius over to his side, but Confucius was of no mind to see him.

阳货趁您不在时，送来烤乳猪。
Yang Huo sent this suckling pig for you while you were out.

只好依礼到他家回谢他了。
Then in accordance with propriety, I'll have to go thank him in person.

孔子趁阳货外出时，登门叩谢，不巧，在中途却碰上了阳货。
Meaning to arrive at the palace while Yang Huo was away, Confucius set out, but as luck would have it, he ran into Yang Huo on the way there.

孔夫子！我和你讲句话！
Confucius! I'd like to speak with you!

保存着自己的学问，而不肯拿出来把国家治理好，可以算是"仁"吗？
Could one say that a person who hides his erudition rather than employing it for the benefit of his country is "benevolent"?

不可以！
No!

一个人希望出来为国做事，但屡次失掉机会，可以算是"智"吗？
And could one say that a person who wishes to serve his country but continually neglects opportunities to do so is "wise"?

不可以！
No!

时间过得真快，岁月是不会等人的呀！
Ah, the seasons pass so quickly, and time waits for no one!

是的，我打算出来做官呀！
Yes. I'm planning to work as a minister of the state!

孔子口头上应付，但还是拒绝辅佐阳货。
Agreeing only in principle, Confucius still refused to assist Yang Huo.

鲁定公八年，阳货决心把三桓的势力连根拔除。
In the eighth year of what was nominally Duke Ding's reign, Yang Huo decided to uproot the Three Huans once and for all.

将三桓灭了，我取而代之。
Destroy the Three Huans. I'll take all their places!

是!
Yes, sir!

三桓为了自己的政治生命，于是联合起来作殊死斗争。
Vying for their political survival, the Three Huans joined forces and fought tooth and nail.

阳货的失败，替孔子制造了一个从政的良机。
Yang Huo's defeat was a golden opportunity for Confucius to reenter government.

阳货终于被三桓打败，离开鲁国，逃到齐国。
In the end, Yang Huo was defeated and subsequently fled to Qi.

季孙氏钦敬孔子不肯附合阳货的正大光明的人格，于是向鲁定公推荐孔子。
Jisun praised Confucius for refusing to assist Yang Huo, and so recommended him to Duke Ding.

鲁定公任孔子为中都宰。
Duke Ding appointed Confucius chief magistrate of the town of Zhongdu.

11

孔子才到职一年就很有绩效，四方的官吏都模仿他的政治。
After only a year at his post, Confucius had a sterling record, with all of the other ministers following his lead.

孔子又由中都宰升任司空，后来又由司空转任大司寇，兼管司法和治安。
He was subsequently promoted to minister of public works, then again to executive minister of justice, in which capacity he oversaw the judicial system and ensured peace and order throughout the country.

鲁国一些专干非法勾当的不肖之徒，都自动改过或者离开鲁国。
With Confucius on the job, all of the country's low-down, rotten, lawless rapscallions either changed of their own accord or quickly beat a path across the border.

由于他以德感人，以礼教民，社会上都尊敬老者；
Because he treated people with virtue and educated people in propriety, everyone respected their elders;

行人男女都分开走路，并且路不拾遗，夜不闭户。
Men and women walked separately in the streets, lost items were let lie, and doors could be left open even at night.

12

鲁定公十年，定公欲与齐修好，齐大夫黎鉏警告齐景公说：
In the tenth year of Duke Ding's reign, the Duke attempted to reconcile with Qi, and hearing this, a nobleman of Qi named Li Chu warned Qi's Duke Jing:

鲁国用了孔丘，他将鲁国治理得很好，鲁国一强盛就会危害到齐国的。
Lu has employed Confucius, who has governed their country extremely well. As Lu grows stronger, they are bound to be a threat to us in the future.

孔丘知礼而无勇，会盟时用莱人劫持鲁侯，孔丘一定没有办法应付。
Confucius may understand propriety, but he is a coward at heart. After the negotiations, I suggest you use the barbarian performers to take the duke prisoner. Confucius will be helpless.

就这么办！派使者去约鲁君来做和好的会盟。
Perfect! Send an emissary to arrange treaty negotiations with Lu.

是！
Yes, sire!

使 *Emissary*

齐景公遣使约我们会盟于夹谷。
Qi's Duke Jing sent an emissary to arrange a treaty summit with us in Jiagu.

好极了，立刻准备轻车上路，到夹谷会盟。
Wonderful. Arrange for a small delegation to leave for Jiagu immediately.

且慢！
Wait!

13

我听说有文事必有武备，有武事者必有文备。
I've heard that for diplomatic affairs, there must also be military readiness, just as for military affairs, there must also be diplomatic readiness.

从前诸侯出了自己的国境，一定带了必要的官员随行，请你也带左右司马一道去。
Whenever noblemen of the past crossed their country's borders, they were always sure to go with a military accompaniment in addition to their diplomatic delegation. I suggest you do likewise.

好。
Fine.

鲁定公就带了孔子与左右司马，出发到夹谷会盟。
So the duke set out for Jiagu with Confucius and a full military complement.

两君在夹谷相会，双方行了相见礼，双方互献酬礼。
Meeting at the appointed place, the two monarchs began by exchanging formalities.

14

献酬礼毕，双方一起写盟书。
Following the formalities, the two sides drew up a treaty together.

齐在盟书上加写了一条……
When the duke of Qi added an unexpected provision...

齐国的军队到国外作战的时候，鲁国要用三百辆兵车协助齐国的军队作战。
In the event that Qi cross its borders to wage war, Lu shall send military assistance in the form of three hundred manned chariots.

约盟鲁齐
Qi-Lu Alliance

孔子不甘示弱，也在盟书上加写一条……
Not wanting to be taken advantage of, Confucius added a provision of his own ...

齐国应将以前侵占鲁国汶水以北的土地归还给鲁国。
All the Qi-occupied land north of the Wen river shall be returned to Lu.

约盟鲁齐
Qi-Lu Alliance

可恶！
Scoundrel!

大王，动手吧。
Do it now, sire.

好！
Right!

请奏四方之乐！
Begin the festivities!

呵呵呵呵！
Ya, ya, ya, ya, ya, ya!

15

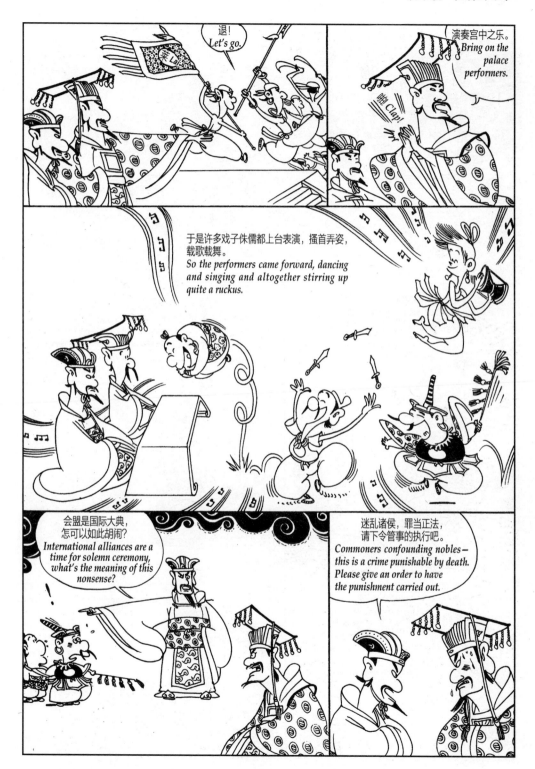

斩了吧!
Off with their heads!

哇!
Ahh!

景公看孔子态度严正，不由得不敬畏动容。
Duke Jing observed Confucius' severe attitude and couldn't help but respect him.

景公回国后，心里很不安……
Upon returning to his country, Duke Jing was extremely upset ...

鲁以君子之道辅助国君，你们却以夷狄之道怂恿我，因而失礼，这下怎么办?
Confucius uses the gentleman's way to assist his sovereign. And you use the barbarian's way to embarrass me. We made fools of ourselves, and now what can we do about it?

小臣该死!
Would that I die, sire!

君子有过，就用具体事物来谢罪；小人有过则用敷衍回报，君上如果心里不安，就只好谨守盟约吧。
If a gentleman errs, he apologizes with his deeds. When an inferior man errs, he compensates with insincerity. If you feel uneasy about what happened, the only way to make up for it is to observe the terms of the treaty.

好吧! 将郓、汶阳、龟阴之田归还给鲁国，用以谢罪。
All right! Return all of our occupied land to Lu as an apology.

是。
Yes, sire.

18

鲁定公十二年夏天……
In the summer of Lu Duke Ding's twelfth year on the throne...

我希望把军权收归国有，建议三桓把三都毁掉。
I'd like to return the military power of the noblemen to the central government and so propose that the Three Huans tear down the walls of their cities.

好。
All right.

我打算拆毁你们三家封邑的城墙，以免再发生阳货事件。
I plan on tearing down the walls of your three cities to prevent another Yang Huo incident from happening.

把三邑的城郭拆了也好，以免家臣以三都作根据地，实行军事叛乱。
That's a good idea. That way our household ministers wouldn't be able to use our cities as bases for revolt.

于是叔孙先把郈的城郭毁掉。
Shusun was the first to destroy his city wall.

公山不狃，令你将军队撤离费城，我要将费的城郭毁掉！
Gongshan Buniu, I order you to remove your troops from the city wall, as our city of Bi shall no longer have a wall!

可恶，季孙氏准备毁了我们的根据地。这要怎么办？
That dastardly Jisun is going to destroy our base of operations. What should we do?

不妙！他怕我们坐大……
It figures! He's afraid we'll take over...

19

好! 一不做二不休, 举兵与他们拼了!
Then we'll finish this once and for all! Muster the troops!

不好了! 公山不狃率领费邑的军队叛变了……
Trouble, sire! Gongshan Buniu has called his troops to battle and is taking over...

定公和三桓都仓皇地躲进季孙氏的城堡中避难……
Duke Ding and the Three Huans took refuge in Jisun's palace...

申句须, 乐颀! 率兵下台攻击他们。
Shen Juxu and Yue Qi, take your troops and suppress them.

费人开始退走, 在姑蔑被彻底打败, 公山不狃等人便逃到齐国。
The Bi army began to retreat and was thoroughly defeated at Gumie, but Gongshan Buniu and his remaining men escaped to Qi.

终于顺利把费城拆毁了。
The city wall at Bi was finally torn down according to plan.

接下来准备拆成城。
O.k., only one more to go.

是!
Yes, sir!

拆了成邑的城，齐人必将进逼到我们北边门户!
If we destroy our city wall, we'll have the Qi people breathing right down our necks!

但成城的邑宰公敛处父对孟孙氏说：
But the warden of the city wall, Gonglian Chufu, objected, saying to Mengsun:

况且成城是你们孟孙氏的保障，没有成城等于没有孟氏了，我打算抗命不拆。
What's more is that that wall is the Mengsuns' guarantee of safety. No wall means no more Mengsun. I refuse to comply.

十二月，定公率兵包围成城，但没有攻下来。
In the twelfth month, Duke Ding mustered his forces and assailed the city, but the siege ended in failure.

21

鲁定公十三年，孔子以大司寇的职位参预国家决策大事，脸上露出得意的神色。
It was the thirteenth year of Duke Ding's reign, when as executive minister of justice Confucius attended the country's policy-making conference and entered with a gloating air about him.

听说一个君子，祸事临头不慌张恐惧，好事到来也不喜形于色。
I've heard that when disaster is imminent, a gentleman does not display fear, and when good fortune comes, he does not display pleasure.

是有这话，但是不也听说过"乐其以贵下人"的话吗？
Yes, someone did say that, but haven't you also heard the saying, "Rejoice in your position over others"?

于是就把扰乱鲁国政事的大夫少正卯给杀了。
Confucius had Shaozheng Mao, the high level official responsible for creating unrest in Lu, executed.

孔子参与国政才三个月，贩羊卖猪的商人就不敢哄抬价钱。
With Confucius participating in policy decisions, after only three months, merchants no longer haggled over prices.

No Second Price.

四方旅客来到鲁国，不向官吏请求也会受到亲切的照顾。
And visitors were welcomed to the country with open arms.

鲁界
Border

观光免签证。
Welcome to Lu, no visa required.

22

23

定公与季桓子果然终日沉迷其间，一连三天都不过问政务。
Duke Ding and Jisun Si spent three days enraptured by the women, oblivious to the affairs of the country.

并且春祭天地大典又违背常礼，没分祭肉给大夫。
In addition to this, the proper ceremony was not followed at the time of the spring sacrifice in that the rightful portions of sacrificial meat were not allotted to the officials.

老师，我们可以离开了。
Master, I think we should leave.

好吧。
Yes.

阳货余党完全清除了，季孙氏的地位巩固，所以不会再重用我了，而鲁君又毫无实权……走了吧。
Yang Huo and his band have been completely wiped out, and Jisun's position firmly established. I fear they'll no longer see a need for me, not to mention that the duke has lost all of his real authority... Let's go.

于是孔子辞去大司寇的职务，离开鲁国到卫国去……
So Confucius resigned his post as minister of justice, departing Lu for the state of Wei...

25

经过匡城的时候，颜刻替孔子赶车……
Yan Ke was driving Confucius' carriage when they passed through the Zheng city of Kuang. Noticing a hole in the wall (by way of which the city had been attacked before) ...

从前我跟阳货就是从那缺口攻进来的。
Once when I came here, I entered through that hole in the wall.

不好了！阳货又来了！阳货这坏蛋又来了！
Oh no! Yang Huo's back! Run for cover! Yang Huo's back!

阳货曾欺虐过匡人，孔子的长相又像阳货，匡人就把孔子一行围困起来……
Yang Huo had terrorized Kuang in the past, and as Confucius resembled Yang Huo in appearance, the people of Kuang encircled him, threatening vengeance...

周文王已经死了，传统文化不就在我这儿吗？如果天意要毁掉这文化，我这后死的人就不能参与了解这文化；
The ancient Zhou King Wen, founder of our culture, is long dead, so don't the traditions of our culture rest on my shoulders? If Heaven wants to destroy this culture, then it will let me die, and the culture will die with me...

如果天意不想毁掉这文化，匡地的人又能把我怎么样呢？
But if Heaven doesn't want to destroy this culture, what can the Kuang people do to me?

27

各国的君子只要和我们国君有交情的，必定会见我们夫人，我们夫人想见你。
It is customary for any gentleman who wants to be on friendly terms with our ruler to meet his wife. Now the duchess would like to meet you.

好。
All right.

这种女人有什么好见的！
Why should he meet with such a woman?!

孔子进了门，向北跪拜行礼，夫人在帷幕里回拜答礼，子路非常不高兴……
Confucius entered, and facing north, he kowtowed to the duchess, a woman of immodest reputation. She returned the gesture, all this annoying Zilu to no end...

我本来不预备见她，既然不得已见了。就得还她以礼。
I originally had no wish to meet her, but since it was expected of me and I went to see her, I had no choice but to bow to her.

哼！
Hmph!

我若是有一点不光明坦白的地方，让上天罚我！
If I transgressed in even the slightest way, may Heaven punish me!

29

过了一个多月，有一天卫灵公和夫人同坐一辆车子游市区，孔子坐第二部车跟着。
Over a month passed, and one day Duke Ling and his wife were riding through the city with Confucius second in the procession.

Wei

好美!
*Wei
Wow,
look
at her!*

美极了!
Gorgeous!

好漂亮!
Beautiful!

我没有见过喜欢美德如同喜欢美色那样热切的人。
I've never seen anyone as interested in the beauty of virtue as they are in the beauty of a woman.

于是对这里的一切感到失望，就离开卫国往曹国去了。
Feeling disappointed about everything in Wei, Confucius departed and set out for the state of Cao.

这一年，鲁定公死了。
That same year, Duke Ding of Lu passed away.

孔子来到郑国，却与弟子们失散了……
With no other choice, Confucius departed and set out for the state of Zheng, but once there, he became separated from his disciples...

东门那里站着一个人，
额头像唐尧，脖子像皋陶，
肩膀像子产，腰以下比禹短了三寸。
At the North gate, there's a man who has a forehead like King Yao of Tang; a neck like Gao Yao, the great minister under King Shun of Yu; shoulders like the great statesman Zichan; and a lower body like the giant-king Yu, only shorter.

一副疲惫倒楣的样子，真像个失去主人家的狗。
He looks dejected and all out of sorts, like a dog that's lost its way home.

老师!
Master!

说我的形貌像谁像谁，
实在不敢当。
I don't deserve to be compared to great men like that,

但说我像丧家之狗，真是对极了!
真是对极了!
But he was right about me being like a dog that's lost its way home. No doubt about that! No doubt about that!

孔子来到了陈国……
Confucius went to the state of Chen...

在司城贞子家里寄住了三年。
Where he stayed for three years at the home of a high official named Sicheng Zhenzi.

正好遇着晋楚两国在争强，一再来攻打陈国；
It so happened that at that time the states of Jin and Chu were competing for supremacy and so time after time battled over Chen.

Wu

Chen

吴国也经常侵犯陈国……
The state of Wu also had a tendency to attack Chen...

回去吧！回去吧！留在家乡的孩子们，志气都大，虽然行事疏略，但有进取心，不忘本。
Sigh. Let's go back. The students back home are ambitious; it's just that they have forgotten how to behave properly. Still though, they are enthusiastic, and they haven't forgotten what's important.

于是孔子就离开了陈国。
So Confucius departed Chen.

33

路过蒲邑，公叔氏占据了蒲而背叛卫国，蒲人就留住了孔子。
Confucius passed through the city of Pu, which one Gongshu had taken control of during a revolt in Wei, and his men confronted Confucius on the road.

我公良孺跟着老师在匡遇难，如今又在这里遇上危难，这是命吧……
Confucius' disciple Gongliang Ru said: I was with you when you encountered trouble in Kuang. Now we're in trouble again; it must be fate...

我和老师一再遭难，宁愿跟他们拼死算了！
But if my master and I are in danger, I'm prepared to fight to the death!

如果你们能不去卫国，我就放你们走。
Look, as long as you don't pass through the capital, I'll let you go.

这样孔夫子一行安然离开。
So Confucius was let pass unharmed.

好吧，一言为定。
It's a deal.

35

有一天卫灵公问起军队战阵的事……
One day, Duke Ling asked Confucius about military affairs...

关于祭祀典礼的事，我倒听说过；至于军队战阵的事，我却不曾学过。
I can tell you about matters pertaining to sacrificial rites, but I'm afraid I've never studied military affairs.

第二天，灵公和孔子谈话，见雁群飞过，只顾抬头仰望，神色间并不注意孔子。
The next day when the duke and Confucius were talking, a flock of wild geese flew by. The duke seemed more interested in the geese than in talking with Confucius.

于是孔子就离开卫，又去陈国。
So Confucius left Wei and went back to Chen.

第二年又从陈国迁到蔡国。
The following year, he left Chen and went to the state of Cai.

孔子离开了叶回到蔡国，又碰上吴国进攻陈国，楚国又来救陈，
Confucius left She and returned to Cai. Here, he again encountered Wu invading Chen and Chu coming to the aid of Chen. And in the midst of all the devastation and confusion,

兵荒马乱之间，孔子竟被困在陈、蔡之间，粮食也断绝了。
Confucius found himself caught between Cai and Chen without access to any food.

随行弟子都饿病了，孔子却照常讲学诵书、弹琴唱歌。
His students began to feel the adverse effects of prolonged hunger, but Confucius continued to teach and recite, to play the zither and sing.

咕 *growl*

君子也会有这样穷困的时候吗？
Is this what being a gentleman comes to?

啪！
Clang!

会有的，只不过君子遭到困穷时，能够坚持品德，小人遭到困穷时，那他便胡作非为！
There will be times like this. But in times of distress, a gentleman perseveres and maintains his dignity, while a lesser man loses control and commits unseemly acts.

鲁哀公十一年，孔子六十八岁，季康子以厚币迎孔子返鲁。
In the eleventh year of Lu Duke Ai, when Confucius was sixty-eight years old, Jisun Fei welcomed Confucius back to Lu with a large emolument.

孔子离鲁周游列国前后有十四年了。
Confucius had been away from Lu traveling the land for fourteen years before returning.

哀公与季康氏虽时从孔子问政，惟终不能用；
Duke Ai and Jisun often asked Confucius about principles of governing, but they never put his suggestions to use.

孔子亦已不在乎求仕了，仅以"国老"家居，续删《诗》《书》、订《礼》《乐》、赞《周易》、修《春秋》……
Confucius no longer entertained visions of becoming a government official, instead utilizing his position as scholar-laureate to compile the Book of Songs and the Book of History, to edit the Book of Ceremony and the Book of Music, to comment on the Book of Changes, and to write the Spring & Autumn Annals...

周易
Book of Changes

春秋
Spring & Autumn Annals

礼乐
Ceremony & Music

诗书
Songs & History

平时则在洙泗之滨讲习，教授门人……
He lectured and taught his disciples between the banks of the Zhu and Si rivers...

他收学生，不分贫富贵贱全部俱收，并且因材施教。
Confucius did not discriminate between rich and poor, high station or low. He accepted all students that came to him, teaching each according to the students ability.

孔子的教学设立了文、行、忠、信四种科目。
Confucius initiated the four teachings: Culture, Conduct, Conscientiousness, Trustworthiness.

文行忠信

又严立格物、致知、诚意、正心、修身、齐家、治国、平天下
八个为学、立身、处世的宗旨。
He also established the eight steps in learning, self-cultivation, and conduct:

Investigation of things
Extension of knowledge
Sincerity of thought
Rectification of the mind
Cultivation of the person
Regulation of the family
Order in the state
Peace throughout the land

格致诚正修齐治平
物知意心身家国天下

更进而通习"礼、乐、射、御、书、数"等六艺、以臻于"智、仁、勇"的三达德。
Furthermore, the students were expected to attain the three virtues of wisdom, benevolence, and courage through their mastery of the six arts: rites, music, archery, charioteering, calligraphy, and mathematics.

孔子教学分为：
志于道、据于德、依于仁、游于艺
四个阶段。
Confucius' teachings can be distinguished into four areas of emphasis:
Resolving yourself on the Way
Residing in virtue
Relying on benevolence
Reveling in the arts

游于艺 依于仁 据于德 志于道

文学
Literature

政事
Governing

言语
Speech

德
Virtue

以德行为首，言语次之，政事又次之，文学列为最末。
Take virtuous conduct as primary, speech as secondary to it, governing as secondary to that, and literature as the last.

41

过了七天，孔子就死了。
Seven days later, Confucius passed away.

孔子死于鲁哀公十六年四月己丑日，享年七十三岁……
He died on the twenty-sixth day of the fourth month, in the sixteenth year of Duke Ai, at the age of seventy-three...

太史公说：《诗经》有这样的话："崇峻的高山，是我们所仰望的；伟大的德行，是我们所取法的。"
The Grand Historian Sima Qian says, "It is written in the Book of Songs thus: 'We emulate virtuous conduct as we look up to lofty mountains.'

"孔子以一介布衣而流传十余世，凡是知识分子没有不以孔子为宗师的，孔子真可算得是至高无上的圣人了！"
Confucius was a commoner whose teachings have been transmitted for more than ten generations, and there is no intellectual who does not consider him his teacher. Confucius was indeed the greatest of all sages!"

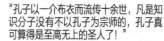

论　语
The Analects

学而时习之
Pleasure and Humi-
lity

学得一种知识而能够应时实行，这不是很令人高兴的吗？
Is it not pleasurable to study and practice what one learns?

有朋友从远方来，不是很令人快乐的吗？
Is it not delightful to have friends come from afar?

即使不见知于人心里也毫不怨恨，这不就是一位有修养的君子吗？
Is he not a gentleman who remains dignified though going unrecognized?

吾日三省吾身
Self-Critique

曾子说：我每天以三件事情反省我自己：
Confucius' pupil Zengzi said: Everyday I critique myself in three ways:

替人谋事，有不忠心的吗？
In helping others, did I not do so conscientiously?

和朋友交往，有不信实的吗？
In intercourse with my friends, was I not trustworthy?

老师所传授的学问，有不温习的吗？
Did I not review what had been taught me before?

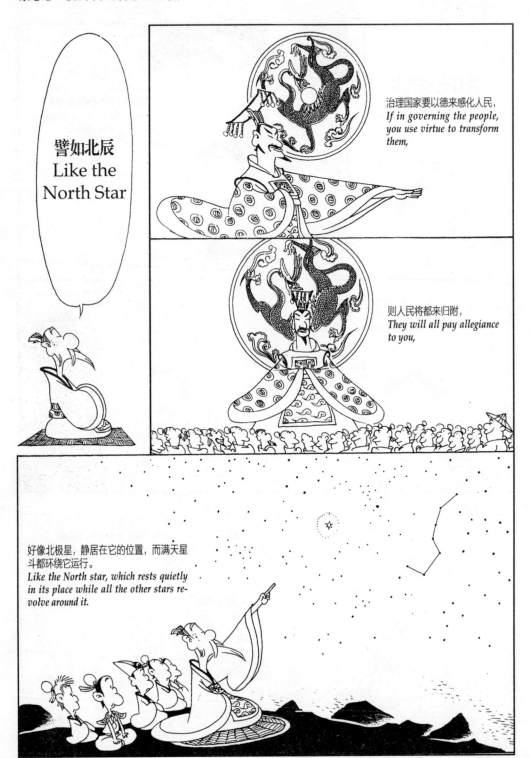

譬如北辰
Like the
North Star

治理国家要以德来感化人民，
*If in governing the people,
you use virtue to transform
them,*

则人民将都来归附，
*They will all pay allegiance
to you,*

好像北极星，静居在它的位置，而满天星
斗都环绕它运行。
*Like the North star, which rests quietly
in its place while all the other stars re-
volve around it.*

48

志于学
Cultivating the
Way

我十五岁时，便立志向学；
When I was fifteen, I set my mind on learning.

到了三十岁，就已经能够坚守所学，毫不动摇了。
When I was thirty, I could hold firm in my learning without the least bit of wavering.

到四十岁，对处理事情和了解道理，已经没有不明白的地方了。
At forty, there was nothing I didn't know about conducting affairs or understanding principles.

五十岁时能够知天命，因而能不怨天、不尤人。
At fifty, I understood the mandates of Heaven, and because of this, I bore no grudge against Heaven nor did I blame others.

到六十岁，只要听到别人一讲话，便能判断这话的是或非，这人的人品如何。
At sixty, I could judge a person's honesty and character simply by hearing them speak.

到了七十岁时，无论一言一行，不必去想，一切都不会做错。
At seventy, I became able to speak and act spontaneously without ever making a mistake.

知之为知之
True
Understanding

知礼
Proper Ceremony

孔子初入周公庙助祭，每件事情都去问人。
One day when Confucius went to the Duke of Zhou Temple to assist in the sacrifice, he inquired about every aspect of the ceremony.

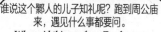

谁说这个鄹人的儿子知礼呢？跑到周公庙来，遇见什么事都要问。
Who said this guy from Zou knows anything about ceremony? He comes to a sacrifice here and asks about every little thing.

遇事皆问，谦虚而不敢自是，这就是礼啊！
Asking questions, being humble rather than presuming to know everything—this is proper ceremony!

饩羊
The Sacrificial Goat

子贡想要把告朔祭所供奉羊的仪式废除。
Confucius' disciple Zigong wanted to eliminate the goat from an ancient sacrificial ceremony that had lost its particular significance.

老师，
把告朔祭的羊省了吧……
Master, can we do without the goat...

赐啊！你是舍不得那只羊，
Si, what you care about is the goat,

我却舍不得那种礼。
What I care about is the ceremony.

士志于道
The Way of
Self-Respect

一个读书人若已立志求道，
If a true student sets his mind on studying the Way,

而还耻于自己穿得不好，
And yet is ashamed of the clothes he wears,

吃得不好，
Or the food he eats,

这种人便不足和他讨论道了！
He is not worth discussing the Way with!

!

53

不患无位
What It
Takes

不愁得不到职位，
Don't worry about not having a position,

该愁的是自己有没有才德担任这项职位。
Worry instead about whether or not you have what it takes to hold a position.

不愁别人不知道我，
Don't worry about other people not knowing about you,

应该责求自己有什么才德可以值得被别人知道的。
Pursue instead qualities that are worth knowing about.

见贤思齐
Seeing
Yourself
in Others

看到贤德的人，想和他看齐；
When you see someone who is capable and virtuous, think about trying to be like him;

看到不贤的人，
When you see someone who is neither capable nor virtuous,

当自我反省，
Look at yourself,

反省自己有没有像他这样不善的行为。
And see if you share any qualities with him.

远游
Traveling

父母在世时，不可出外远游。
While your parents are still living, do not travel far away.

如果不得已要出外远游，应将
去向告诉父母，以免父母忧心。
If you have no choice but to travel far away, let your parents know your whereabouts so that they won't worry.

德不孤
Friends
of Virtue

有德行的人不会孤独；
A man who has virtue will never be lonely;

必定有声气相同的人来亲近他的。
Others like himself will always be near.

57

颜回之智
Yan Hui's Intellect

孔子对子贡说：
One day, Confucius said to Zigong:

你与颜回哪一个比较强？
Who is better, you or Yan Hui?

我怎么比得上颜回呢？
How can I be compared with Yan Hui?

颜回听得一件道理，便能推知全体，彻底明了，
If you tell Yan Hui one thing, he can extrapolate ten more things from that.

我听得一件道理，只能推知两件。
If you tell me something, I can only figure out two more things.

你是不如他，我和你都不如他啊！
You're right, you're not as good as he is. Neither you nor I are as good as he is.

谓之"文"
The Meaning of "Cultured"

巧言令色
Contriving Appear-ances

说阿谀好听的话，装出谄媚讨人喜欢的脸色，过分地卑恭，
To speak flattering words, to contrive an ingratiating appearance, and to be overly respectful...

这个样子，左丘明认为可耻，我也认为可耻。
The scholar Zuoqiu Ming found this kind of behavior shameful. I, too, find it shameful.

心里怨恨一个人，表面却和他友善……
To insincerely befriend a person you really detest ...

这种事情，左丘明认为可耻，我也认为可耻。
Zuoqiu Ming found this kind of behavior shameful. I, too, find it shameful.

言志
Wishes

颜渊、子路陪侍孔子。
One day when Yan Yuan and Zilu were accompanying Confucius...

何不各说说自己的志愿呢？
Why don't each of you tell me what you have your minds set on.

我愿意把我的车、马、衣、裘和朋友共用，就是用坏了，也不怨恨。
I wish to be able to lend my horses and carriage, clothes and furs to others, and if they get ruined, to not regret having lent them.

我愿不夸耀自己的长处，
I wish to not boast about my strengths

不表白自己的功劳。
and to not shirk my troubles off on others.

我们也想听听老师的志愿。
We also wish to hear what the master has his mind set on.

我愿意让年老的人都能得到奉养而安乐，
For old people to be well cared for,

朋友之间互相信赖，
Friends to be trustworthy,

年少的都能得到抚爱。
And children to be cherished.

十室之邑
A Town of Ten Families

只有十户人家的小地方，
In a small town of only ten families,

必定会有像我这样忠信的人，
There is sure to be someone whose conscientiousness and trustworthiness match mine,

只是没有像我这样好学罢了。
There just won't be anyone who likes to learn as much as me.

颜回好学
Yan Hui's Learning

鲁哀公问孔子说：
One day, Duke Ai of Lu asked Confucius:

你的学生里面哪一个最好学？
Which one of your students likes to learn the most?

有个叫颜回的最为好学：
There was one called Yan Hui who most enjoyed learning.

他若发怒，便会立刻化解；
If he ever lost his temper, he realized it and steadied himself immediately;

他犯了过，决不会再犯。
And he never made the same mistake twice.

不幸短命死了！现在就没有再见过这样好学的人。
Unfortunately, he died young. And I have yet to find one who enjoys learning as much as him.

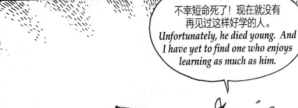

颜回之贤
Yan Hui's Worthiness

颜回真是贤德啊！
Yan Hui was certainly capable and virtuous!

一小碗饭，
A small bowl of rice,

一瓢水，
A ladleful of water,

住简陋狭窄的屋子，
And a run-down cottage.

别人都受不了这种穷苦，而颜回却没有改变他自得的乐趣。
Other people can't take such poverty, but it never affected Yan Hui's cheerfulness.

颜回真是贤德啊！……
Yan Hui was certainly capable and virtuous!

仁者与智者
The Wise and The Benevolent

有智慧的人通达事理，所以喜欢周流无滞的水。
Wise people enjoy the water. They understand the happenings of the world and so take pleasure in the smooth flowing of the water.

有仁德的人安于义理，所以喜爱厚重不移的山。
Benevolent people enjoy the mountains. They are steadfast in their virtue and so take pleasure in the unwavering of the mountains.

有智慧的人好动。
Wise people enjoy being active.

有仁德的人好静。
Benevolent people enjoy keeping still.

有智慧的人自得其乐。
Wise people find their own joys.

有仁德的人恬淡而长寿。
Benevolent people live long in tranquillity.

66

述而不作
Transmitting
Ideas

传述旧闻而不创作。
I transmit ideas rather than create them.

笃信尧舜禹汤文武的道理，而喜欢古时的文化。
I believe in the principles of the Tang, Yu, Xia, Shang, and Zhou founders and take delight in ancient culture.

私下效法商朝的贤大夫老、彭。
And I privately emulate Old Peng, the capable and virtuous minister of the Shang dynasty.

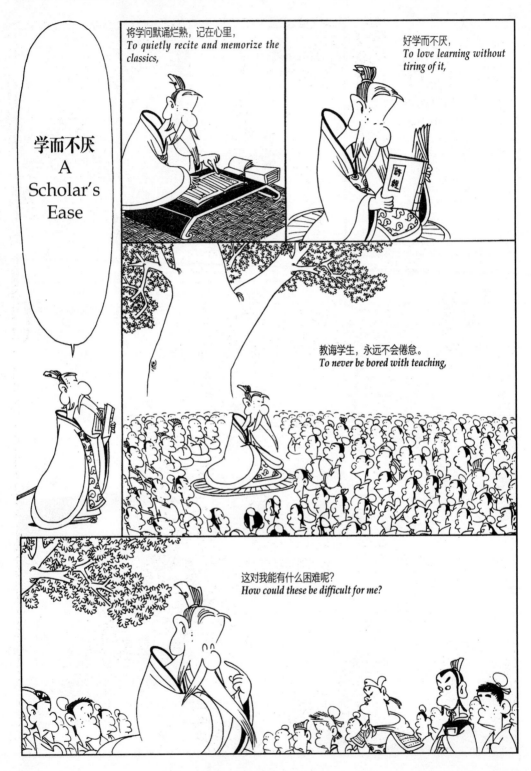

学而不厌
A Scholar's Ease

将学问默诵烂熟，记在心里，
To quietly recite and memorize the classics,

好学而不厌，
To love learning without tiring of it,

教诲学生，永远不会倦怠。
To never be bored with teaching,

这对我能有什么困难呢?
How could these be difficult for me?

梦见周公
Dreaming of the Duke of Zhou

我已衰老极了……
Oh, I'm getting so old...

很久很久，我都没有梦见周公了！
It's been so long since I dreamed of the Duke of Zhou!

志于道
The Foundation of Good Conduct

做人的目标，应合乎大道；
Resolve yourself on the Way;

道
Way

做事的根据，应把握住德性；
Rely on virtue;

人生应遵循着仁爱的方向；
Reside in benevolence;

而涵泳于六艺之中。
Revel in the arts.

未尝无诲
Universal
Education

凡是能自动奉送一些敬师礼品而来的人，
For anyone who brings even the smallest token of appreciation,

我没有不收他做学生而教诲他的。
I have yet to refuse instruction.

不愤不启
Teaching
Good Students

没到了因求知而烦懑的，我不会去启发他。
If a student does not feel troubled in his studies, I don't enlighten him.

没到了因求知而怅恨的，我是不会去开导他。
If a student does not feel frustrated in his studies, I don't explain to him.

如果举一个角给他，
If I point out one corner,

他不能推想到其他三个角，就不再教导他了。
And he can't point out the other three, I don't continue instructing him.

乐朴
Simple
Pleasures

吃粗淡的饭，
Eating coarse rice,

喝白开水，
Drinking plain water,

弯着手臂当作枕头，乐趣就在其中了。
Bending my arms around as a pillow—
this is where joy lies.

不合于正道的富贵，对我来说，就像天上的浮云一样。
To me, wealth and nobility gained through unsavory means are like
clouds drifting in the sky.

好学
Knowledge
and Study

我并不是生下来就什么都知道的；
I wasn't born with the knowledge I have;

我只是好读古书，
I just like to study the ancient books,

用敏捷的心思，勤快地研求来的。
And I pursue their ideas with a keen mind.

三人行，
必有我师
Learning
from Others

三个人同行，这里面一定有可以做我的老师的。
If there are three people walking along, there will certainly be one I can learn from.

选择他们的长处加以学习；
I notice their strong points and work to emulate them;

他们的短处也可作自我改正的参考。
I also notice their defects and try to change if I find them in myself as well.

哈 Ha,
哈 Ha,
哈 Ha,

酒
Wine

酒
Wine

酒
Wine

钓而不纲
Fair Play

孔子用钓竿钓鱼，
Confucius would use a fishing pole to catch fish,

但不用大网网鱼；
But he wouldn't use a net.

孔子射鸟，
He'd shoot birds,

但不射夜里栖息的鸟。
But not while they were nesting.

人之将死，其言也善
Dying Men Don't Lie

曾子病了；孟敬子来看他。
One day when Zengzi was ill, Meng Jingzi paid a visit to him.

鸣
tweet

鸟将死的时候，它的鸣声是悲哀的；
The sound of a bird about to die is melancholy;

人将死的时候，他说的话是诚恳善意的。
The words of a man about to die are honest.

君子所重的道有三项：
There are three things that a gentlemen should emphasize in regard to the Way:

容貌举动要合乎礼，才能远离粗厉放肆；端正颜色，才能不妄而近于诚信；言辞合理得体，才能远离鄙陋悖理。至于一切礼节上的定例，自有专管的人员在。
By keeping your facial expressions and demeanor in accord with propriety, you can distance yourself from coarseness and frivolity; by maintaining a sober countenance, you can keep from being reckless and you can approach sincerity; by speaking reasonably and properly, you can distance yourself from shallow and absurd prattlings. As for all of the various aspects of ceremony, there are people to perform them.

学如不及
Good Students
Fear
Forgetting

求学就像来不及似的，
When studying, it always seems like there's not enough time,

学到了又怕把它失掉。
And once something is learned, there's always the fear of losing it.

逝者如斯
The
Stream of
Time

人世一切的消逝，也就是像这样的吧！
All things that pass are just like this!

不分日夜，永无止息。
Night and day, it never stops.

后生可畏
Age and Respect

年轻人是不可以小看的；
Young people should not be taken lightly;

我们怎料得到他们的将来比不上我们这一辈人的现在呢？
Who's to say that someday they won't surpass our own generation?

不过，假如一个人到了四十或五十岁仍没有成就，
However, if a person has reached forty or fifty years-old and is still without accomplishment,

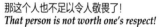

那这个人也不足以令人敬畏了！
That person is not worth one's respect!

知者不惑
Facing
Facts

有智慧的人不会疑惑；
A wise person will never feel perplexed.

有仁德的人不会忧虑；
A benevolent person will never worry.

有勇气的人不会恐惧。
And a brave person fears nothing.

厚焚
Fire in the
Stable

孔子的马房失火了。
One day, Confucius' stable caught fire.

孔子退朝回来，他说：
Confucius hurried home from the court, and the first words out of his mouth were:

烧伤了人没有？
Is anyone hurt?

不问马有没有烧伤。
He didn't ask about the horses.

过犹不及
Overdoing It

子张和子夏哪一个比较贤能？
Which one is more capable and virtuous, Zizhang or Zixia?

子张超过了些……
Zizhang overdoes it. . .

子夏又稍嫌不足一点。
And Zixia falls short.

那么是子张比较强一点啰？
Then Zizhang is the better one?

太过和不及，同样的不好！
Overdoing it is still falling short!

柴也愚
Chai Is
Naive

高柴的性子愚直，
Gao Chai is naive,

曾参的性子迟钝，
Zeng Shen is slow,

颛孙师其志过
高而流於一偏，
Zhuansun Shi
is biased,

仲由的性子太刚猛。
And Zhong You is
hot-tempered.

颜回是比较有希望能
成就的，只是常困於
贫穷！
Yan Hui seems to have
the most promise for
success; it's just that
he is often hampered
by poverty!

端木赐不受教命而做生意，却能每次猜中物
价的涨跌，而赚了大钱。
And then there is Duanmu Ci, who does business instead of receiving instruction. Still,
he guesses right once at the direction prices
will go and earns a large sum of money.

仁
Benevolence

四海皆兄弟
Brothers

司马牛很忧伤地对子夏说：
One day when Confucius' disciple Sima Niu was quite distraught, he addressed Zixia saying:

别人都有兄弟，我独没有！
Everyone else has brothers, and I seem to be the only one who doesn't!

我听说过："人的生死是命中注定的，人的富贵也是上天安排的。"
Someone once said, "Life and death are due to fate; wealth and poverty are arranged by Heaven."

一个有才德的君子，只要内心敬谨而不要有什么过失，待人恭敬有礼，
If a gentleman is deferential and cautious, if he treats others with respect and propriety,

那么，天下人都可以算是你的兄弟了。
Then everyone will consider him his brother.

一个君子何必担心没有兄弟呢？
How can a gentleman worry about not having brothers?

以文会友
Making
Friends

曾子说：
君子用礼貌来交友；
Zengzi said:
A gentleman makes friends through his culture;

用朋友来帮助自己修养仁德。
And through his friends, he cultivates his own benevolence.

Benevolence

正己
Rectifying
Oneself

如果自己做得正，治理政事又有什么困难呢？
If one can rectify one's person, what problems can there be in governing?

如果自己不能做得正，又怎能纠正别人？
If one cannot rectify one's person, how can one rectify others?

欲速则不达
Patience and Prescience

子夏做莒父的宰官，
Zixia gained a position as prefect of Jufu.

他向孔子请教为政的道理。
One day, he asked Confucius about the principles of governing.

不要求速成，不要只看到小利益；
Do not hurry success; do not focus on expediency.

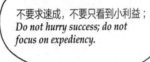

求速成，就不能达成任务，
If you hurry success, you will fail in your duties;

只看到小利益，
就不能完成大事。
If you focus on expediency, you will not accomplish great things.

问耻
Greed Is Shameful

成人
The Complete Person

怎样才算是才德兼备的成人？
What is a complete person?

要有像臧武仲那样的智慧，
Someone who has the intelligence of the wise official Zang Wuzhong,

孟公绰的不贪欲，
The uncovetousness of Meng Gongchuo,

卞庄子的勇敢，
The courage of Zhuangzi of Bian,

冉求的才艺；并且熟悉礼乐，就可以算是成人了。
And the talent of Ran Qiu, together with a knowledge of propriety and music, can be considered complete.

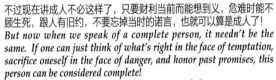

不过现在讲成人不必这样了，只要财利当前而能想到义，危难时能不顾生死，跟人有旧约，不要忘掉当时的诺言，也就可以算是成人了！
But now when we speak of a complete person, it needn't be the same. If one can just think of what's right in the face of temptation, sacrifice oneself in the face of danger, and honor past promises, this person can be considered complete!

言行
Saying
and
Doing

说大话不惭愧的人，
If one whose speaking of it is immodest,

要他实践就难了！
his carrying it out will be difficult!

耻其言而过
其行
Extravagant
in Deeds

君子说话不敢说得过分，
A gentleman is modest in words,

我将尽力而为。
I'll do my best.

却往往做的超过他所说的。
And extravagant in deeds.

做得又多又好。
He does a lot, and he does it well.

评头论足
Throwing Stones

千里马
A Good
Horse

千里马受称赞并不是因它有好脚力，
A good horse is praised not for its strength,

而是因它的德性驯良。
But for its virtue.

以直报怨
How to Treat
One's Enemies

知我者
Understanding
Confucius

没有人能够了解我吧！
No one understands me!

为什么没有人能够了解老师呢！
How come no one understands you, master?

我既不怨恨天，也不责怪人，只是从人事上去学习，
I bear no grudge against Heaven, and I do not blame others. I learn from the affairs of people,

了解我的恐怕只有天吧！
Perhaps the only one who understands me is Heaven!

从浅近处下功夫，渐渐能向上领悟天理；
Applying myself to simple things at hand, and gradually I understand the principles of Heaven.

知其不可而为之
Stubborn

子路在石门城外住了一夜。
Zilu once put up for the night outside of Shimen in Qi.

喂喂
Excuse me.

就是那明知做不成功却一定要去做的那个人吗?
Oh, you mean the one who knows he won't succeed but keeps on anyway?

你从哪里来的?
Where are you from?

从孔家来。
I come from the house of Confucius.

老而不死
A Wasted Life

孔子的老朋友原壤看到孔子来了，蹲在那儿等着。
Once when Confucius' old acquaintance Yuan Rang saw Confucius coming, he disrespectfully crouched down and waited for him.

你小的时候不晓得谦顺孝悌；
When you were young, you didn't understand humility or respect for elders;

长大了也没什么表现；
As an adult you had no accomplishments;

如今老了还不死，真是祸害！
And now you're old and refuse to die. What a disgrace!

就顺手用拐杖敲他的脚胫。
With this, he rapped the man on the shin with his cane.

wack

102

有道则仕
Conditional
Service

史鱼真是个正直的人！国家政治清明时，他忠心任职，像箭一般正直；
Shi Yu certainly is an upright and straightforward person! When the government is just, he dutifully takes his position. He's as straight as an arrow.

国家政治昏乱时，他正言直谏！也像箭一般正直。
When the government is corrupt, he tells it like it is! He's as straight as an arrow.

蘧伯玉可算是个君子啊！国家政治清明时，他就出来做官；
Qu Boyu certainly is a gentleman! When the government is just, he works as a minister,

国家政治昏乱时，就收藏起自己的才能而隐退。
And when the government is corrupt, he conceals his talents and goes off by himself.

为仁
Cultivating
Benevolence

子贡问怎样修养
仁德。
Zigong asked
Confucius how
to cultivate
benevolence in
oneself.

工匠要做好他的工
作，一定先要磨快他
所用的工具。
Before an artisan
does his job, he must
always grind his
tools first.

住在一个国家里，应该
在贤能的官吏下服务。
Living in any country,
one should serve under
a capable and
virtuous
minister.

应该结交有仁德的士人。
And make friends with
benevolent officers.

人无远虑，
必有近忧
Thinking
Ahead

一个人做任何事，如果不做深远的考虑，
In any matter, if one doesn't think far into the future,

忧患就会随时降临。
Trouble will be near at hand.

己所不欲，勿施于人
The Golden Rule

思与学
Thinking vs.
Studying

我曾经整天不吃饭，
*In the past, I have gone all day
without eating,*

整夜不睡觉……
Gone all night without sleeping . . .

而专心思考；却徒劳无功，
*And spent all my time thinking;
but to no avail.*

还不如脚踏实地地去学习的好。
It is better to study.

107

当仁不让
Yield to
No One

如遇到行仁的事，
When an opportunity to practice benevolence arises,

对于师长也不必谦让。
Do not yield even to your teacher.

抱歉! 这件
行仁义的事让我去做!
Excuse me! But I believe I can handle this matter of benevolence!

君子三戒
The Three
Temptations

君子有三件事要戒慎：
年轻的时候，血气未稳定，
所以要戒的是色欲；
There are three things a gentleman must abstain from: In youth, when the vital fluids have yet to stabilize, the abstention is lust.

到了壮年，血气正旺，
所以要戒的是好勇斗狠；
In middle age, when the vital fluids are fully potent, the abstention is contentiousness.

到了老年，血气已衰，所以要戒的是贪得无厌。
In old age, when the vital fluids have subsided, the abstention is acquisitiveness.

君子九思
The Nine Considerations

君子有九种应当用心思虑的：
There are nine considerations a gentleman should keep in mind:

看要想看得明白，
When listening, be mindful of acuity,

礼
prosperity

听要想听得清楚，
When looking, be mindful of clarity,

脸色要想表现得温和，
For facial expressions, be mindful of geniality,

容貌要想到谦恭，
For demeanor, be mindful of deference,

忠实……
Be sincere...

说话要想到忠实，
When speaking, be mindful of sincerity,

做事要想到恭敬，
When acting, be mindful of reverence,

疑惑要想到发问，
When confused, be mindful of inquiring,

忿怒要想到后患，
When angry, be mindful of the consequences,

见到利要想到是否应得。
When seeing the chance for gain, be mindful of what is right.

诚不以富
Praising Deeds

《诗经》上说："称道人并不因他富有，只因他的德行和常人不同。"
A passage from the Book of Songs says that people aren't praised for their wealth but for their extraordinary actions.

齐景公有马四千匹，到他死的时候，百姓并不觉得他有什么值得称述的善行。
Duke Jing of Qi had four thousand horses, but when he died, the people felt no reason to praise him.

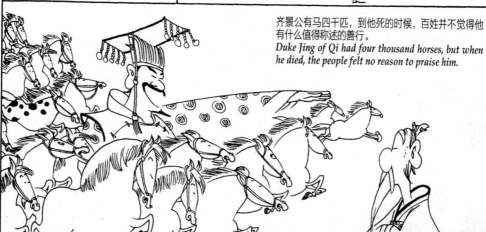

伯夷、叔齐虽饿死在首阳山下，人们到现在还称赞他们。"诚不以富，亦只以异。"就是说这种情形吧！
On the other hand, although Boyi and Shuqi (brothers who refused the crown out of principle) starved to death at the foot of Shou-yang Mountain, people praise them even now. Do not the lines, Praise stems not from prosperity, and only from the extraordinary. Refer to this?

性相近，
习相远
Nature vs.
Nurture

一般人的本性原是相似的，
Peoples original natures are
nearly the same,

由于教育和生活
环境的不同，
But due to
different
educations and
environments,

使每个人的差异愈来愈显著了。
They grow farther and farther apart.

六弊
The Six Defects

仲由啊，你听过六种美德并随着六种流弊的说法吗？
Zhong You, have you heard about how the six virtues can become the six defects?

没有。
No, I haven't.

坐下！我告诉你。
Sit down, and I'll tell you.

是。
Yes, master.

喜欢仁爱却不好学，便会流于愚昧；
喜欢聪明却不好学，便会流于放荡；
喜欢诚实却不好学，便会遭受戕害；
喜欢正直却不好学，便会有急切的毛病；
喜欢勇敢却不好学，便会招致祸乱；
喜欢刚强却不好学，便会有狂躁的毛病。

To love benevolence but not love learning is to slip into foolishness;
To love wisdom but not love learning is to slip into vagaries;
To love sincerity but not love learning is to encounter harm;
To love forthrightness but not love learning is to become rash;
To love courage but not love learning is to invite disaster;
To love strength but not love learning is to become wild.

113

穿窬之盗
The Brazen
Burglar

一个人在外表上假装得很威严的样子，
A person who puts on brazen airs,

而内心却软弱没有志气，
While being cowardly on the inside,

这种欺世盗名之辈若用小民作比喻，
Compared to people from lower walks of life,

就像挖壁跳墙的小偷一样，实在可耻啊！
Is like the shameless burglar that digs a whole or scales a wall.

115

玩乐
Playing
Games

一个人整天吃饱了饭，却一点心思也不用；
Someone who, having eaten his fill, goes about all day without using his mind at all

这种生活决难有所成就的。
Will have difficulty ever accomplishing anything.

不是还有玩双陆和下围棋的游戏吗？就是做这些也比整天不用一点心思还要好些啊！
Aren't there those who play games all day? This is still better than not using your mind at all!

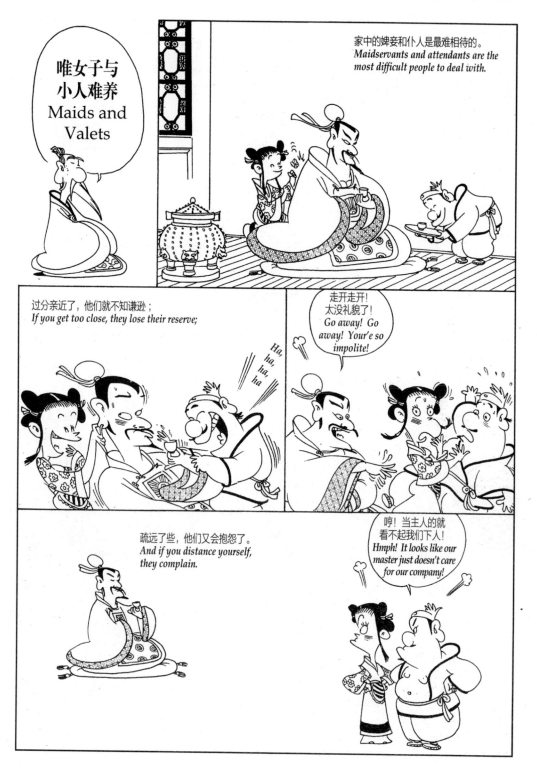

四十而见恶
An Imma-
ture Forty

混蛋!
Take that!

一个人到了四十岁时，还显现恶行，
Someone who is forty years old and still goes about acting wickedly,

他的这一生也就做不出什么好事了!
Will never do a single decent thing his whole life!

仁者之责
Benevolence and Duty

商纣暴虐无道，他的哥哥微子便离开他；
The infamous last emperor of the Shang dynasty was a horrible and depraved tyrant. Because of this, his brother, the Viscount of Wei, left him;

另一个叔叔比干更因苦谏不听，而遭剖腹而死。
And another uncle named Bigan admonished him repeatedly and was finally eviscerated.

他的叔叔箕子因直言劝谏而被囚禁起来，做了奴隶；
His uncle, the Viscount of Ji, was locked up and made a slave because he dared to admonish him;

商朝末年有三位伟大的仁人啊！
The Shang dynasty had three benevolent men!

所以孔子非常赞叹地说：
Approving of the mens conduct, Confucius said:

119

狂人接舆
Crazy Jieyu

楚国的狂人接舆唱着歌走过孔子的车前，
A man from Chu named Jieyu, who pretended to be crazy to avoid government service, passed by Confucius one day singing a song:

凤鸟啊！凤鸟啊！你的运命为什么这么坏？过去的不可挽回了，但未来的还可以赶得上啊……
Oh, phoenix! Oh, phoenix!
How virtue has declined!
You can't get back the past,
But you can still catch up with the future...

算了吧！算了吧！现在从政的人都很危险呀！
Forget it! Forget it!
Being an official now is all too dangerous!

孔子下车想和接舆谈谈；但他却很快地避开，因此孔子就无法跟他谈话了。
Confucius descended from his carriage hoping to talk with Jieyu. Jieyu, however, quickly departed the area before Confucius could say anything.

两位隐者
The Two Recluses

长沮和桀溺两人在田里耕作，孔子刚好经过那里。
One day when the two recluses Chang Ju and Jie Ni were out working their fields, Confucius happened to pass by.

去请问他们过河的渡口在哪里。
Go ask them where we can cross the river.

是。
Yes, master.

请问渡口在什么地方？
Could you please tell me where we may cross the river?

那位在车上拉着缰绳的人是谁呢？
Who is that in the carriage holding the reins?

君子之过
Being an
Example

君子的过失，就像日蚀月蚀一样。他有
过失人人都看得见。
*A gentleman's transgressions are like
an eclipse of the sun or moon. When it
happens, everyone can see it,*

等到过失改正之后，大家仍都瞻仰他。
*And when its corrected, everyone looks
up in high regard.*

孔子的弟子
The Disciples of Confucius

我的学生中，道艺精通的弟子有七十七人，他们各有特出的才能和成就。
Of my students, there are seventy-seven who are well-versed in the arts, and each of them has his own accomplishments.

长于政事的有冉有、季路；
Those whose strength lies in governing are Ran You and Ji Lu.

长于德性的有颜渊、闵子骞、冉伯牛、仲弓；
Those whose strength lies in virtuous conduct are Yan Yuan, Min Ziqian, Ran Boniu, and Zhonggong.

长于言语的有宰我、子贡；
Those whose strength lies in speaking are Zai Wo and Zigong.

长于文学的有子游、子夏。
And those whose strength lies in culture and learning are Ziyou and Zixia.

颜回字子渊，鲁国人，小孔子三十岁。
Surname: Yan
Given name: Hui
Coming of age name: Ziyuan
Home state: Lu
Years younger than Confucius:thirty

颜回才二十九岁，头发就已全白了，三十二岁就死了，他死时孔子哭得很伤心。
At the age of twenty-nine, Yan Hui's hair had already turned white, and he passed away when he was only thirty-two. At his death, Confucius wept with momentous grief.

老师……别哭得太悲痛了！
Master...please... try not to feel so bad...

唉！我这大道没得传了，我完了！我完了！
Oh, my! I'll never be able to transmit the Way. I'm finished! I'm finished!

真的过于悲痛吗？不为他悲痛，还要为谁悲痛呢？
Am I really grieving too much? If I don't grieve for him, who else is there to grieve for?

127

闵损字子骞，鲁国人，小孔子十五岁。
Surname: Min
Given name: Sun
Coming of age name: Ziqian
Home state: Lu
Years younger than Confucius: fifteen

孔子赞美道："闵子骞真是个孝子啊！他顺事父母，友爱兄弟，
Confucius praised Min Ziqian, saying:
Min Ziqian certainly practices filial virtue! He serves his
parents and loves his brothers,

叫旁人对他的父母兄弟都没有非议的闲话。"
Nobody has anything but praise for how he
treats his parents and brothers.

他守身自爱，不出任权臣的家臣，不接受坏国君的俸禄。所以他对季氏的使者说：
He had great self-respect and integrity. He didn't
serve as household minister under powerful offi-
cials, nor did he accept emoluments from foreign
nobles. It is for these reasons that he said to a fo-
reign emissary:

如果再来召我的话，
那我就渡过汶水出国去了。
If you come looking for me
again, I'll be forced to cross
the Wen river and leave the
country altogether.

128

冉雍字仲弓，鲁国人，小孔子二十九岁。他的家世不好，父亲是个身份卑贱的人。
Surname: Ran
Given name: Yong
Coming of age name: Zhonggong
Home state: Lu
Years younger than Confucius: twenty-nine Came from a lower class family

即使是耕牛所生的小牛，只要是毛色纯赤，头角端正，就具备了做牺牛的体德。
Even though it is merely the offspring of a plow ox, as long as it has a pure cinnabar coat and its horns are symmetrical, it is qualified to be used in a sacrificial ceremony.

虽然人们顾忌它的出身低而不用来做祭牛，
And although someone may object due to its humble origins,

但山川的神灵难道肯舍弃它而不歆飨吗？
Would the gods of the mountains and rivers ever refuse such an offering?

129

仲由字子路，是卞地方的人，小孔子九岁。他本来很粗野，喜欢逞勇斗力，气性刚猛爽直，后来终受孔子的感化。子路晚年出任卫国蒲邑的大夫，卫国发生变乱，仲由就死于卫乱中。

Surname: Zhong
Given name: You
Coming of age name: Zilu
Home state: Lu, Bian county
Years younger than Confucius: nine
With an inflammatory and straightforward character, he was originally a coarse and unrefined man who enjoyed fighting and exhibiting his bravery. He was transformed by Confucius. In his later years, he held the position of chief magistrate of the city of Pu in Wei. He was killed during a rebellion that swept through Wei.

仲由的学问已经登上正大光明的境地，只是还没进入精微深密的领域罢了。
Zhong You's studies have achieved a certain level of enlightenment; it's just that they have yet to attain that realm of profundity.

穿了破旧袍子跟穿着狐貉皮衣的人站在一起，而不觉寒酸难为情的，恐怕只有仲由了吧！
To wear worn clothes and stand next to someone wearing furs and leather yet not feel the least bit ashamed- I'm afraid only Zhong You would be capable of that!

宰予字子我，鲁国人，这个人口齿伶俐，能言善辩。宰予出任齐国的临菑大夫，参与田常的乱事，后来因罪全家遇害，孔子很为他不值。

Surname: Zai

Given Name: Yu

Coming of age name: Ziwo

Home state: Lu

Age difference with Confucius unknown

With a sharp tongue and quick wit, this man was a fine speaker and a good debater. Zai Yu held the position of chief magistrate of Linzi, and because he participated in the Tian Chang uprising, he and his entire family were destroyed. He also lost favor with Confucius.

131

端木赐字子贡，卫国人，小孔子三十一岁。
他口才好，能言善辩，爱宣扬别人的长处，却也不隐匿人家的过失。不止
一次帮助鲁、卫两国解除困局。家境富裕，善于做生意，拥有千金财产，
晚年死在齐国。
Surname: Duanmu
Given name: Si
Coming of age name: Zigong
Home state: Wei
Years younger than Confucius: thirty-one
Eloquent, a fine speaker, and a good debater, he enjoyed praising other
people's merits, but at the same time, he would not ignore their transgressions. More than once he helped Lu and Wei resolve stalemates. He
came from a wealthy family, and being good at
business, he built up riches of a thousand gold
pieces. He died late in the state of Qi.

卜商字子夏，是温地方的人，小孔子四十五岁。孔子逝世以后，子夏定居在魏国的西河地方，教授生徒，成了魏文侯的老师。后来他儿子死了，伤心得眼睛都哭瞎了。

Surname: Pu
Given name: Shang
Coming of age name: Zixia
Home state: Wei, Wen region
Years younger than Confucius: forty-four
After Confucius died, Zixia took up residence in the Xihe region of Wei, where he began teaching and attracting followers of his own. He also became the personal tutor to Marquis Wen of Wei.
His son died young, and his grief over it caused him to cry himself blind.

古诗上说："巧笑倩兮，美目盼兮，素以为绚兮。"诗中这三句话是指什么？
In the ancient songs it says:
Lovely smile and cheeks white
Beautiful eyes clear and bright
Plainness makes the pattern right
What do these three lines mean?

是说作画时，要先要素底，然后再加上五彩的颜色。
They mean that when you paint, you first prepare a plain ground, and then you add the pattern.

由此看来，人先要有美德，然后用礼来修饰吗？
So what you are saying is that people must first possess virtue, and then they should add propriety as adornment.

你这话启发了我，像你这样颖悟的人，才可以与你谈诗呀！
You have enlightened me! Poetry can only be discussed with extremely bright people like yourself!

澹台灭明字子羽，是武城人，小孔子三十九岁。子羽体态面貌长得很丑，但为人方正规矩，后来他游历到江南，追随他的学生有三百人之多，他订定了个人取予的原则，绝不苟且，所以清誉传遍了四方诸侯。

Surname: Tantai
Given name: Mieming
Coming of age name: Ziyu
Home state: Lu, city of Wu
Years younger than Confucius: thirty-nine
Ziyu was known to have a physique and countenance that were quite ugly. Despite this, however, he was a man of integrity. He traveled to southern China with a following of about three hundred disciples. He established a code of conduct for them, which he himself never violated. For these reasons, his sterling reputation spread to noblemen in the four corners of the land.

子游做了武城的邑宰。
Ziyou was the chief magistrate of the city of Wu.

你在那里有没有得到贤能的人来协助？
Have you had the help of any capable and virtuous men there?

有个叫澹台灭明的人，做人循规蹈矩从不抄小路捷径，
There is one called Tantai Mieming who is strictly law-abiding. He never takes short-cuts,

如果不是为了公事，他从来不到我的住处。
And he only comes to my residence for official business.

134

曾参字子舆，鲁国南武城人，小孔子四十六岁。孔子认为他能通达孝道，所以传授他学业。他著了《孝经》一书，晚年死于鲁国。

Surname: Zeng
Given name: Shen
Coming of age name: Ziyu
Home state: Lu, southern part of the city of Wu
Years younger than Confucius: forty-six
Confucius saw in him a great propensity toward filial virtue and so transmitted to him all that he knew about the subject. Zeng Shen then wrote the Book of Filial Virtue. He died late in the state of Lu.

孝经
Book of Filial Virtue

135

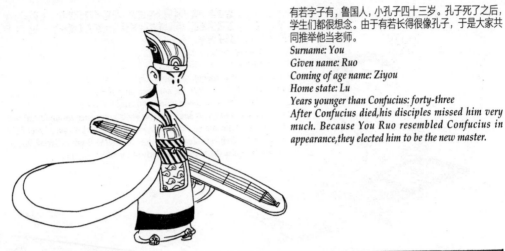

有若字子有，鲁国人，小孔子四十三岁。孔子死了之后，学生们都很想念。由于有若长得很像孔子，于是大家共同推举他当老师。
Surname: You
Given name: Ruo
Coming of age name: Ziyou
Home state: Lu
Years younger than Confucius: forty-three
After Confucius died,his disciples missed him very much. Because You Ruo resembled Confucius in appearance,they elected him to be the new master.

礼的行使，以和为可贵！
The practice of propriety should emphasize harmony.

古时圣王之道以和为美，不论小事大事都依照和去做。
The way of the kings of antiquity, in affairs small and large, was to act according to harmony.

和

但也有行不通的！
But this in itself did not assure success.

只知和为美，而不以礼来节制，那也会行不通的。
If harmony is not regulated by propriety, it cannot be put into practice.

礼 *propriety*

和 *harmony*

136

南宫括字子容，鲁国人。孔子谈起子容时说："国家政治清明时，他不至于没有职位，国家政治昏乱时，他又能明哲保身，不会遭受祸害。"孔子就把哥哥的女儿嫁给他。

Surname: Nangong
Given name: Kuo
Coming of age name: Zirong
Home state: Lu
Age difference with Confucius unknown
Confucius said in regard to Zirong, When the government is just, he will certainly hold a post. When the government is in chaos, he will maintain his integrity and protect
himself from harm. Confucius married his own niece to him.

羿擅长射箭，界很会荡舟，两人徒尚勇力，但都不得好死。
Hou Yi was a great archer, and Ao could row a boat over land. Both of them were mighty and courageous, but neither died a natural death.

夏禹和后稷却不这样，他们亲自下田耕种，反而得到了天下，是不是这样？
Xia Yu and Hou Ji, however, were not like this. They personally tilled the fields and ended up being lords of the whole land. Isn't that right?

孔子没有回答，子容就退出去了。
Confucius didn't answer, and Zirong departed.

这个人真是一位君子！真是一位崇尚德性的人啊！
This man is truly a gentleman! How he esteems virtue!

公西赤字子华，鲁国人，小孔子四十二岁。
Surname: Gongxi
Given name: Chi
Coming of age name: Zihua
Home state: Lu
Years younger than Confucius: forty-two

子华奉派出使齐国，冉有替子华的
母亲向孔子请求安家米粮。
Once when Zihua was sent as an
emissary to the state of Qi, Ran
You asked for some grain on behalf
of Zihua's mother.

给他六斗四升吧。
Give her a bushel
of grain.

再多给他
一些吧!
Shouldn't we give
her more than
that?

那就再给他
十六斗吧。
All right. Giver
her two and a
half bushels.

冉有却自作主张给了他八百斗。
Ran You disregarded what Confu-
cius said and gave her 130 bushels.

孔子知道了，说：
After Confucius found out, he said:

公西赤这次出使齐国，坐着肥马拉的车，
穿着轻暖的裘衣。我听说：
一个君子是周济人家的急难，而不是增加他的财富。
For this trip to Qi, Gongxi Chi wears light furs
and drives a carriage pulled by a fat horse. I have
heard that a gentleman aids people in distress but
does not add to another persons wealth.

附录·延伸阅读
APPENDIX Further reading

此部分为本书图画页的延伸阅读，各段首所示的页码与图画页对应。

P1—P44　孔子生鲁昌平乡陬邑。其先宋人也，曰孔防叔。防叔生伯夏，伯夏生叔梁纥。纥与颜氏女野合而生孔子，祷于尼丘得孔子。鲁襄公二十二年而孔子生。生而首上圩顶，故因名曰丘云。字仲尼，姓孔氏。

丘生而叔梁纥死，葬于防山。防山在鲁东，由是孔子疑其父墓处，母讳之也。孔子为儿嬉戏，常陈俎豆，设礼容。孔子母死，乃殡五父之衢，盖其慎也。陬人挽父之母诲孔子父墓，然后往合葬于防焉。

孔子要绖，季氏飨士，孔子与往。阳虎绌曰："季氏飨士，非敢飨子也。"孔子由是退。

孔子年十七，鲁大夫孟厘子病且死，诫其嗣懿子曰："孔丘，圣人之后，灭于宋。其祖弗父何始有宋而嗣让厉公。及正考父佐戴、武、宣公，三命兹益恭，故鼎铭云："一命而偻，再命而伛，三命而俯，循墙而走，亦莫敢余侮。饘于是，粥于是，以餬余口。"其恭如是。吾闻圣人之后，虽不当世，必有达者。今孔丘年少好礼，其达者欤？吾即没，若必师之。"及厘子卒，懿子与鲁人南宫敬叔往学礼焉。是岁，季武子卒，平子代立。

孔子贫且贱。及长，尝为季氏史，料量平；尝为司职吏而畜蕃息。由是为司空。已而去鲁，斥乎齐，逐乎宋、卫，困于陈蔡之间，于是反鲁。孔子长九尺有六寸，人皆谓之"长人"而异之。鲁复善待，由是反鲁。

鲁南宫敬叔言鲁君曰："请与孔子适周。"鲁君与之一乘车，两马，一竖子俱，适周问礼，盖见老子云。辞去，而老子送之曰："吾闻富贵者送人以财，仁人者送人以言。吾不能富贵，窃仁人之号，送子以言，曰："聪明深察而近于死者，好议人者也。博辩广大危其身者，发人之恶者也。为人子者毋以有己，为人臣者毋以有己。"孔子自周反于鲁，弟子稍益进焉。

是时也，晋平公淫，六卿擅权，东伐诸侯；楚灵王兵强，陵轹中国；齐大而近于鲁。鲁小弱，附于楚则晋怒；附于晋则楚来伐；不备于齐，齐师侵鲁。

鲁昭公之二十年，而孔子盖年三十矣。齐景公与晏婴来适鲁，景公问孔子曰："昔秦穆公国小处辟，其霸何也？"对曰："秦，国虽小，其志大；处虽辟，行中正。身举五羖，爵之大夫，起累绁之中，与语三日，授之以政。以此取之，虽王可也，其霸小矣。"景公说。

孔子年三十五，而季平子与郈昭伯以斗鸡故得罪鲁昭公，昭公率师击平子，平子与孟氏、叔孙氏三家共攻昭公，昭公师败，奔于齐，齐处昭公乾侯。其后顷之，鲁乱。孔子适齐，为高昭子家臣，欲以通乎景公。与齐太师语乐，闻《韶》音，学之，三月不知肉味，齐人称之。

景公问政孔子，孔子曰："君君，臣臣，父父，子子。"景公曰："善哉！信如君不君，臣不臣，父不父，子不子，虽有粟，吾岂得而食诸！"他日又复问政于孔子，孔子曰："政在节财。"景公说，将欲以尼溪田封孔子。晏婴进曰："夫儒者滑稽而不可轨法；倨傲自顺，不可以为下；崇丧遂哀，破产厚葬，不可以为俗；游说乞贷，不可以为国。自大贤之息，周室既衰，礼乐缺有间。今孔子盛容饰，繁登降之礼，趋详之节，累世不能殚其学，当年不能究其礼。君欲用之以移齐俗，非所以先细民也。"后景公敬见孔子，不问其礼。异日，景公止孔子曰："奉子以季氏，吾不能。"以季孟之间待之。齐大夫欲害孔子，孔子闻之。景公曰："吾老矣，弗能用也。"孔子遂行，反乎鲁。

孔子年四十二，鲁昭公卒于乾侯，定公立。定公立五年，夏，季平子卒，桓子嗣立。季桓子穿井得土缶，中若羊，问仲尼云"得狗"。仲尼曰："以丘所闻，羊也。丘闻之，木石之怪夔、罔阆，水之怪龙、罔象，土之怪坟羊。"

吴伐越，堕会稽，得骨节专车。吴使使问仲尼："骨何者最大？"仲尼曰："禹致群神于会稽山，防风氏后至，禹杀而戮之，其节专车，此为大矣。"吴客曰："谁为神？"仲尼曰："山川之神足以纲纪天下，其守为神，社稷为公侯，皆属于王者。"客曰："防风何守？"仲尼曰："汪罔氏之君守封、禺之山，为厘姓。在虞、夏、商为汪罔，于周为长翟，今谓之大人。"客曰："人长几何？"仲尼曰："僬侥氏三尺，短之至也。长者不过十之，数之极也。"于是吴客曰："善哉圣人！"

桓子嬖臣曰仲梁怀，与阳虎有隙。阳虎欲逐怀，公山不狃止之。其秋，怀益骄，阳虎执怀。桓子怒，阳虎因囚桓子，与盟而释之。阳虎由此益轻季氏。季氏亦僭于公室，陪臣执国政，是以鲁自大夫以下皆僭离于正道。故孔子不仕，退而修诗书礼乐，弟子弥众，至自远方，莫不受业焉。

定公八年，公山不狃不得意于季氏，因阳虎为乱，欲废三桓之适，更立其庶孽阳虎素所善者，遂执季桓子。桓子诈之，得脱。定公九年，阳虎不胜，奔于齐。是时孔子年五十。

公山不狃以费畔季氏，使人召孔子。孔子循道弥久，温温无所试，莫能己用，曰："盖周文武起丰镐而王，今费虽小，傥庶几乎！"欲往。子路不说，止孔子。孔子曰："夫召我者岂徒哉？如用我，其为东周乎！"然亦卒不行。

其后定公以孔子为中都宰，一年，四方皆则之。由中都宰为司空，由司空为大司寇。

定公十年春，及齐平。夏，齐大夫黎鉏言于景公曰："鲁用孔丘，其势危齐。"乃使使告鲁为好会，会于夹谷。鲁定公且以乘车好往。孔子摄相事，曰："臣闻有文事者必有武备，有武事者必有文备。古者诸侯出疆，必具官以从。请具左右司马。"定公曰："诺。"具左右司马。会齐侯夹谷，为坛位，土阶三等，以会遇之礼相见，揖让而登。献酬之礼毕，齐有司趋而进曰："请奏四方之乐。"景公曰："诺。"于是旄旌羽祓矛戟剑拨鼓噪而至。孔子趋而进，历阶而登，不尽一等，举袂而言曰："吾两君为好会，夷狄之乐何为于此！请命有司！"有司却之，不去，则左右视晏子与景公。景公心作，麾而去之。有顷，齐有司趋而进曰："请奏宫中之乐。"景公曰："诺。"优倡侏儒为戏而前。孔子趋而进，历阶而登，不尽一等，曰："匹夫而营惑诸侯者罪当诛！请命有司！"有司加法焉，手足异处。景公惧而动，知义不若，归而大恐，告其群臣曰："鲁以君子之道辅其君，而子独以夷狄之道教寡人，使得罪于鲁君，为之奈何？"有司进对曰："君子有过则谢以质，小人有过则谢以文。君若悼之，则谢以质。"于是齐侯乃归所侵鲁之郓、汶阳、龟阴之田以谢过。

定公十三年夏，孔子言于定公曰："臣无藏甲，大夫毋百雉之城。"使仲由为季氏宰，将堕三都。于是叔孙氏先堕郈。季氏将堕费，公山不狃、叔孙辄率费人袭鲁。公与三子入于季氏之宫，登武子之台。费人攻之，弗克，入及公侧。孔子命申句须、乐顺下伐之，费人北。国人追之，败诸姑蔑。二子奔齐，遂堕费。将堕成，公敛处父谓孟孙曰："堕成，齐人必至于北门。且成，孟氏之保鄣，无成是无孟氏也。我将弗堕。"十二月，公围成，弗克。

定公十四年，孔子年五十六，由大司寇行摄相事，有喜色。门人曰："闻君子祸至不惧，福至不喜。"孔子曰："有是言也。不曰'乐其以贵下人'乎？"于是诛鲁大夫乱政者少正卯。与闻国政三月，粥羔豚者弗饰贾；男女行者别于途；途不拾遗；四方之客至乎邑者不求有司，皆予之以归。

齐人闻而惧，曰："孔子为政必霸，霸则吾地近焉，我之为先并矣。盍致地焉？"黎鉏曰："请先尝沮之；沮之而不可则致地，庸迟乎！"于是选齐国中女子好者八十人，皆衣文衣而舞《康乐》，文马三十驷，遗鲁君。陈女乐文马于鲁城南高门外。季桓子微服往观再三，将受，乃语鲁君为周道游，往观终日，怠于政事。子路曰："夫子可以行矣。"孔子曰："鲁今且郊，如致膰乎大夫，则吾犹可以止。"桓子卒受齐女乐，三日不听政；郊，又不致膰俎于大夫。孔子遂行，宿乎屯。而师己送，曰："夫子则非罪。"孔子曰："吾歌可夫？"歌曰："彼妇之口，可以出走；彼妇之谒，可以死败。盖优哉游哉，维以卒岁！"师己反，桓子曰："孔子亦何言？"师己以实告。桓子喟然叹曰："夫子罪我以群婢故也夫！"

孔子遂适卫，主于子路妻兄颜浊邹家。卫灵公问孔子："居鲁得禄几何？"对曰："奉粟六万。"卫人亦致粟六万。居顷之，或谮孔子于卫灵公。灵公使公孙余假一出一入。孔子恐获罪焉，居十月，去卫。

将适陈，过匡，颜刻为仆，以其策指之曰："昔吾入此，由彼缺也。"匡人闻之，以为鲁之阳虎。阳虎尝暴匡人；匡人于是遂止孔子。孔子状类阳虎，拘焉五日。颜渊后，子曰："吾以汝为死矣。"颜渊曰："子在，回何敢死！"匡人拘孔子益急，弟子惧。孔子曰："文王既没，文不在兹乎？天之将丧斯文也，后死者不得与于斯文也。天之未丧斯文也，匡人其如予何！"孔子使从者为宁武子臣于卫，然后得去。

去即过蒲。月余，反乎卫，主蘧伯玉家。灵公夫人有南子者，使人谓孔子曰："四方之君子不辱欲与寡君为兄弟者，必见寡小君。寡小君愿见。"孔子辞谢，不得已而见之。夫人在絺帷中。孔子入门，北面稽首。夫人自帷中再拜，环佩玉声璆然。孔子曰："吾乡为弗见，见之礼答焉。"子路不说。孔子矢之曰："予所不者，天厌之！天厌之！"居卫月余，灵公与夫人同车，宦者雍渠参乘，出，使孔子为次乘，招摇市过之。孔子曰："吾未见好德如好色者也。"于是丑之，去卫，过曹。是岁，鲁定公卒。

孔子去曹适宋，与弟子习礼大树下。宋司马桓魋欲杀孔子，拔其树。孔子去。弟子曰："可以速矣。"孔子曰："天生德于予，桓魋其如予何！"

孔子适郑，与弟子相失，孔子独立郭东门。郑人或谓子贡曰："东门有人，其颡似尧，其项类皋陶，其肩类子产，然自要以下不及禹三寸，累累若丧家之狗。"子贡以实告孔子。孔子欣然笑曰："形状，末也。而谓似丧家之狗，然哉！然哉！"

孔子遂至陈，主于司城贞子家。岁余，吴王夫差伐陈，取三邑而去。赵鞅伐朝歌。楚围蔡，蔡迁于吴。吴败越王勾践会稽。

有隼集于陈廷而死，楛矢贯之，石砮，矢长尺有咫。陈湣公使使问仲尼。仲尼曰："隼来远矣，此肃慎之矢也。昔武王克商，通道九夷百蛮，使各以其方贿来贡，使无忘职业。于是肃慎贡楛矢石砮，长尺有咫。先王欲昭其令德，以肃慎矢分大姬，配虞胡公而封诸陈。分同姓以珍玉，展亲；分异姓以远方职，使无忘服。故分陈以肃慎矢。"试求之故府，果得之。

孔子居陈三岁，会晋楚争强，更伐陈，及吴侵陈，陈常被寇。孔子曰："归与归与！吾党之小子狂简，进取不忘其初。"于是孔子去陈。

过蒲，会公叔氏以蒲畔，蒲人止孔子。弟子有公良孺者，以私车五乘从孔子。其为人长贤，有勇力，谓曰："吾昔从夫子遇难于匡，今又遇难于此，命也已。吾与夫子再罹难，宁斗而死。"斗甚疾。蒲人惧，谓孔子曰："苟毋适卫，吾出子。"与之盟，出孔子东门。孔子遂适卫。子贡曰："盟可负邪？"孔子曰："要盟也，神不听。"

卫灵公闻孔子来，喜，郊迎。问曰："蒲可伐乎？"对曰："可。"灵公曰："吾大夫以为不可。今蒲，卫之所以待晋楚也，以卫伐之，无乃不可乎？"孔子曰："其男子有死之志，妇人有保西河之志。吾所伐者不过四五人。"灵公曰："善。"然不伐蒲。

灵公老，怠于政，不用孔子。孔子喟然叹曰："苟有用我者，期月而已，三年有成。"孔子行。

佛肸为中牟宰。赵简子攻范、中行，伐中牟。佛肸畔，使人召孔子。孔子欲往。子路曰："由闻诸夫子，'其身亲为不善者，君子不入也'。今佛肸亲以中牟畔，子欲往，如之何？"孔子曰："有是言也。不曰坚乎，磨而不磷；不曰白乎，涅而不淄。我岂匏瓜也哉，焉能系而不食？"

孔子击磬。有荷蒉而过门者，曰："有心哉，击磬乎！硁硁乎，莫己知也夫而已矣！"

孔子学鼓琴师襄子，十日不进。师襄子曰："可以益矣。"孔子曰："丘已习其曲矣，未得其数也。"有间，曰："已习其数，可以益矣。"孔子曰："丘未得其志也。"有间，曰："已习其志，可以益矣。"孔子曰："丘未得其为人也。"有间，有所穆然深思焉，有所怡然高望而远志焉。曰："丘得其为人，黯然而黑，几然而长，眼如望羊，如王四国，非文王其谁能为此也！"师襄子辟席再拜，曰："师盖云《文王操也》。"

孔子既不得用于卫，将西见赵简子。至于河而闻窦鸣犊、舜华之死也，临河而叹曰："美哉水，洋洋乎！丘之不济此，命也夫！"子贡趋而进曰："敢问何谓也？"孔子曰："窦鸣犊，舜华，晋国之贤大夫也。赵简子未得志之时，须此两人而后从政；及其已得志，杀之乃从政。丘闻之也，刳胎杀夭则麒麟不至郊，竭泽涸渔则蛟龙不合阴阳，覆巢毁卵则凤皇不翔。何则？君子讳伤其类也。夫鸟兽之于不义也尚知辟之，而况乎丘哉！"乃还息乎陬乡，作为《陬操》以哀之。而反乎卫，入主蘧伯玉家。

他日，灵公问兵陈。孔子曰："俎豆之事则尝闻之，军旅之事未之学也。"明日，与孔子语，见蜚雁，仰视之，色不在孔子。孔子遂行，复如陈。

夏，卫灵公卒，立孙辄，是为卫出公。六月，赵鞅内太子蒯聩于戚。阳虎使太子絻，八人衰绖，伪自卫迎者，哭而入，遂居焉。冬，蔡迁于州来。是岁鲁哀公三年，而孔子年六十矣。齐助卫围戚，以卫太子蒯聩在故也。

夏，鲁桓厘庙燔，南宫敬叔救火。孔子在陈，闻之，曰："灾必于桓厘庙乎？"已而果然。

秋，季桓子病，辇而见鲁城，喟然叹曰："昔此国几兴矣，以吾获罪于孔子，故不兴也。"顾谓其嗣康子曰："我即死，若必相鲁；相鲁，必召仲尼。"后数日，桓子卒，康子代立。已葬，欲召仲尼。公之鱼曰："昔吾先君用之不终，终为诸侯笑。今又用之，不能终，是再为诸侯笑。"康子曰："则谁召而可？"曰："必召冉求。"于是使使召冉求。冉求将行，孔子曰："鲁人召求，非小用之，将大用之也。"是日，孔子曰："归乎归乎！吾党之小子狂简，斐然成章，吾不知所以裁之。"子赣知孔子思归，送冉求，因诫曰"即用，以孔子为招"云。

冉求既去，明年，孔子自陈迁于蔡。蔡昭公将如吴，吴召之也。前昭公欺其臣迁州来，后将往，大夫惧复迁，公孙翩射杀昭公。楚侵蔡。秋，齐景公卒。

明年，孔子自蔡如叶。叶公问政，孔子曰："政在来远附迩。"他日，叶公问孔子于子路，子路不对。孔子闻之，曰："由，尔何不对曰'其为人也，学道不倦，诲人不厌，发愤忘食，乐以忘忧，不知老之将至'云尔。"

去叶，反于蔡。长沮、桀溺耦而耕，孔子以为隐者，使子路问津焉。长沮曰："彼执舆者为谁？"子路曰："为孔丘。"曰："是鲁孔丘与？"曰："然。"曰："是知津矣。"桀溺谓子路曰："子为谁？"曰："为仲由。"曰："子，孔丘之徒与？"曰："然。"桀溺曰："悠悠者天下皆是也，而谁以易之？且与其从辟人之士，岂若从辟世之士哉！"耰而不辍。子路以告孔子，孔子怃然曰："鸟兽不可与同群。天下有道，丘不与易也。"

他日，子路行，遇荷蓧（音 diào）丈人，曰："子见夫子乎？"丈人曰："四体不勤，五谷不分，孰为夫子！"植其杖而芸。子路以告，孔子曰："隐者也。"复往，则亡。

孔子迁于蔡三岁，吴伐陈。楚救陈，军于城父。闻孔子在陈蔡之间，楚使人聘孔子。孔子将往拜礼，陈蔡大夫谋曰："孔子贤者，所刺讥皆中诸侯之疾。今者久留陈蔡之间，诸大夫所设行皆非仲尼之意。今楚，大国也，来聘孔子。孔子用于楚，则陈蔡用事大夫危矣。"于是乃相与发徒役围孔子于野。不得行，绝粮。从者病，莫能兴。孔子讲诵弦歌不衰。子路愠见曰："君子亦有穷乎？"孔子曰："君子固穷，小人穷斯滥矣。"

子贡色作。孔子曰："赐，尔以予为多学而识之者与？"曰："然。非与？"孔子曰："非也。予一以贯之。"

孔子知弟子有愠心，乃召子路而问曰："《诗》云：'匪兕匪虎，率彼旷野。'吾道非邪？吾何为于此？"子路曰："意者吾未仁邪？人之不我信也。意者吾未知邪？人之不我行也。"孔子曰："有是乎！由，譬使仁者而必信，安有伯夷、叔齐？使知者而必行，安有王子比干？"

子路出，子贡入见。孔子曰："赐，《诗》云：'匪兕匪虎，率彼旷野。'吾道非邪？吾何为于此？"子贡曰："夫子之道至大也，故天下莫能容夫子。夫子盖少贬焉？"孔子曰："赐，良农能稼而不能为穑，良工能巧而不能为顺。君子能修其道，纲而纪之，统而理之，而不能为容。今尔不修尔道而求为容。赐，而志不远矣！"

子贡出，颜回入见。孔子曰："回，《诗》：云'匪兕匪虎，率彼旷野。'吾道非邪？吾何为于此？"颜回曰："夫子之道至大，故天下莫能容。虽然，夫子推而行之，不容何病，不容然后见君子！夫道之不修也，是吾丑也。夫道既已大修而不用，是有国者之丑也。不容何病，不容然后见君子！"孔子欣然而笑曰："有是哉颜氏之子！使尔多财，吾为尔宰。"

于是使子贡至楚。楚昭王兴师迎孔子，然后得免。

昭王将以书社地七百里封孔子。楚令尹子西曰："王之使使诸侯有如子贡者乎？"曰："无有。""王之辅相有如颜回者乎？"曰："无有。""王之将率有如子路者乎？"曰："无有。""王之官尹有如宰予者乎？"曰："无有。""且楚之祖封于周，号为子男五十里。今孔丘述三五之法，明周召之业，王若用之，则楚安得世世堂堂方数千里乎？夫文王在丰，武王在镐，百里之君卒王天下。今孔丘得据土壤，贤弟子为佐，非楚之福也。"昭王乃止。其秋，楚昭王卒于城父。

楚狂接舆歌而过孔子，曰："凤兮凤兮，何德之衰！往者不可谏兮，来者犹可追也！已而已而，今之从政者殆而！"孔子下，欲与之言。趋而去，弗得与之言。

于是孔子自楚反乎卫。是岁也，孔子年六十三，而鲁哀公六年也。

其明年，吴与鲁会缯，征百牢。太宰嚭召季康子。康子使子贡往，然后得已。

孔子曰："鲁卫之政，兄弟也。"是时，卫君辄父不得立，在外，诸侯数以为让。而孔子弟子多仕于卫，卫君欲得孔子为政。子路曰："卫君待子而为政，子将奚先？"孔子曰："必也正名乎！"子路曰："有是哉，子之迂也！何其正也？"孔子曰："野哉由也！夫名不正则言不顺，言不顺则事不成，事不成则礼乐不兴；礼乐不兴，则刑罚不中；刑罚不中，则民无所措手足"。夫君子为之必可名，言之必可行。君子于其言，无所苟而已矣。"

其明年，冉有为季氏将师，与齐战于郎，克之。季康子曰："子之于军旅，学之乎？性之乎？"冉有曰："学之于孔子。"季康子曰："孔子何如人哉？"对曰："用之有名；播之百姓，质诸鬼神而无憾。求之至于此道，虽累千社，夫子不利也。"康子曰："我欲召之，可乎？"对曰："欲召之，则毋以小人固之，则可矣。"而卫孔文子将攻太叔，问策于仲尼。仲尼辞不知，退而命载而行，曰："鸟能择木，木岂能择鸟乎！"文子固止。会季康子逐公华、公宾、公林，以币迎孔子，孔子归鲁。

孔子之去鲁凡十四岁而反乎鲁。

鲁哀公问政，对曰："政在选臣。"季康子问政，曰："举直错诸枉，则枉者直。"康子患盗，孔子曰："苟子之不欲，虽赏之不窃。"然鲁终不能用孔子，孔子亦不求仕。

孔子之时，周室微而礼乐废，《诗》《书》缺。追迹三代之礼，序《书传》，上纪唐虞之际，下至秦缪，编次其事。曰："夏礼吾能言之，杞不足征也。殷礼吾能言之，宋不足征也。足，则吾能征之矣。"

观殷夏所损益，曰："后虽百世可知也，以一文一质。周监二代，郁郁乎文哉。吾从周。"故《书传》《礼记》自孔氏。

孔子语鲁大师："乐其可知也。始作翕如，纵之纯如，皦如，绎如也，以成。""吾自卫反鲁，然后乐正，《雅》《颂》各得其所。"

古者《诗》三千余篇，及至孔子，去其重，取可施于礼义，上采契、后稷，中述殷、周之盛，至幽厉之缺，始于衽席，故曰"《关雎》之乱以为《风》始，《鹿鸣》为《小雅》始，文王为《大雅》始，《清庙》为《颂》始"。三百五篇孔子皆弦歌之，以求《韶》《武》《雅》《颂》之音。礼乐自此可得而述，以备王道，成六艺。

孔子晚而喜《易》，序《彖》《系》《象》《说卦》《文言》。读《易》，韦编三绝。曰："假我数年，若是，我于易则彬彬矣。"

孔子以诗书礼乐教，弟子盖三千焉，身通六艺者七十有二人。如颜浊邹之徒，颇受业者甚众。

孔子以四教：文，行，忠，信。绝四：毋意，毋必，毋固，毋我。所慎：齐，战，疾。子罕言利与命与仁。不愤不启，举一隅不以三隅反，则弗复也。

其于乡党，恂恂似不能言者。其于宗庙朝廷，辩辩言，唯谨尔。朝，与上大夫言，訚訚如也；与下大夫言，侃侃如也。

入公门，鞠躬如也；趋进，翼如也。君召使傧，色勃如也。君命召，不俟驾行矣。

鱼馁，肉败，割不正，不食。席不正，不坐。食于有丧者之侧，未尝饱也。

是日哭，则不歌。见齐衰、瞽者，虽童子必变。

"三人行，必得我师。""德之不修，学之不讲，闻义不能徙，不善不能改，是吾忧也。"使人歌，善，则使复之，然后和之。子不语：怪，力，乱，神。

子贡曰："夫子之文章，可得闻也。夫子言天道与性命，弗可得闻也已。"颜渊喟然叹曰："仰之弥高，钻之弥坚。瞻之在前，忽焉在后。夫子循循然善诱人，博我以文，约我以礼，欲罢不能。既竭我才，如有所立，卓尔。虽欲从之，蔑由也已。"达巷党人曰："大哉孔子，博学而无所成名。"子闻之曰："我何执？执御乎？执射乎？我执御矣。"牢曰："子云：'不试，故艺。'"

鲁哀公十四年春，狩大野。叔孙氏车子鉏商获兽，以为不祥。仲尼视之，曰："麟也。"取之。曰："河不出图，雒不出书，吾已矣夫！"颜渊死，孔子曰："天丧予！"及西狩见麟，曰："吾道穷矣！"喟然叹曰："莫知我夫！"子贡曰："何为莫知子？"子曰："不怨天，不尤人，下学而上达，知我者其天乎！"

"不降其志，不辱其身，伯夷、叔齐乎！"谓"柳下惠、少连降志辱身矣"。谓"虞仲、夷逸隐居放言，行中清，废中权"。"我则异于是，无可无不可。"

子曰："弗乎弗乎，君子病没世而名不称焉。吾道不行矣，吾何以自见于后世哉？"乃因《史记》做《春秋》，上至隐公，下讫哀公十四年，十二公。据鲁，亲周，故殷，运之三代。约其文辞而指博。故吴楚之君自称王，而《春秋》贬之曰'子'；践土之会实召周天子，而《春秋》讳之曰'天王狩于河阳'：推此类以绳当世。贬损之义，后有王者举而开之。《春秋》之义行，则天下乱臣贼子惧焉。

孔子在位听讼，文辞有可与人共者，弗独有也。至于为'春秋'，笔则笔，削则削，子夏之徒不能赞一辞。弟子受《春秋》，孔子曰："后世知丘者以《春秋》，而罪丘者亦以《春秋》。"

明岁，子路死于卫。孔子病，子贡请见。孔子方负杖逍遥于门，曰："赐，汝来何其晚也？"孔子因叹，歌曰："太山坏乎！梁柱摧乎！哲人萎乎！"因以涕下。谓子贡曰："天下无道久矣，莫能宗予。夏人殡于东阶，周人于西阶，殷人两柱间。昨暮予梦坐奠两柱之间，予始殷人也。"后七日卒。

孔子年七十三，以鲁哀公十六年四月己丑卒。

哀公诔之曰："旻天不吊，不慭遗一老，俾屏余一人以在位，茕茕余在疚。呜呼，哀哉！尼父，毋自律！"子贡曰："君其不没于鲁乎！夫子之言曰：'礼失则昏，名失则愆。失志为昏，失所为愆。'生不能用，死而诔之，非礼也。称'余一人'，非名也。"

孔子葬鲁城北泗上，弟子皆服三年。三年心丧毕，相诀而去，则哭，各复尽哀；或复留。唯子赣庐于冢上，凡六年，然后去。弟子及鲁人往从冢而家者百有余室，因命曰孔里。鲁世世相传以岁时祠孔子冢，而诸儒亦讲礼乡饮大射于孔子冢。孔子冢大一顷。故所居堂弟子内，后世因庙藏孔子衣冠琴车书，至于汉二百余年不绝。高皇帝过鲁，以太牢祠焉。诸侯乡相至，常先谒然后从政。

孔子生鲤，字伯鱼。伯鱼年五十，先孔子死。

伯鱼生伋，字子思，年六十二。尝困于宋。子思作《中庸》。

子思生白，字子上，年四十七。子上生求，字子家，年四十五。子家生箕，字子京，年四十六，子京生穿，字子高，年五十一。子高生子慎，年五十七，尝为魏相。

子慎生鲋，年五十七，为陈王涉博士，死于陈下。

鲋弟子襄，年五十七。尝为孝惠皇帝博士，迁为长沙太守。长九尺六寸。

子襄生忠，年五十七。忠生武，武生延年及安国。安国为今皇帝博士，至临淮太守，蚤卒。安国生卬，卬生驩。

太史公曰：诗有之："高山仰止，景行行止。"虽不能至，然心乡往之。余读孔氏书，想见其为人。适鲁，观仲尼庙堂车服礼器，诸生以时习礼其家，余祗回留之不能去云。天下君王至于贤人众矣，当时则荣，没则已焉。孔子布衣，传十余世，学者宗之。自天子王侯，中国言六艺者折中于夫子，可谓至圣矣！

以上录自汉司马迁《史记·孔子世家》

P45 《论语》是谁写的？谁编的？东汉班固在《汉书·艺文志·六艺略》中有所说明：

"《论语》者，孔子应答弟子、时人，及弟子相与言，而接闻于夫子之语也。当时弟子各有所记，夫子既卒，门人相与辑而论纂，故谓之《论语》。"

由此认为：《论语》是孔子和他的门人或时人的谈话，以及门人彼此的谈话记录。

P46 学而时习之，不亦说乎？有朋自远方来，不亦乐乎？人不知而不愠，不亦君子乎？

《学而》第一——一

P47 曾子曰："吾日三省吾身：为人谋，而不忠乎？与朋友交，而不信乎？传，不习乎？"

《学而》第一——四

P48 为政以德，譬如北辰，居其所，而众星共之。

《为政》第二——一

P49 吾十有五而志于学；三十而立；四十而不惑：五十而知天命；六十而耳顺；七十而从心所欲，不逾矩。

《为政》第二——四

P50 子曰："由，诲女，知之乎？知之为知之，不知为不知，是知也。"

《为政》第二——十七

P51 子入大庙，每事问。或曰："孰谓鄹人之子知礼乎？入大庙，每事问。"子闻之曰："是礼也！"

《八佾》第三 — 十五

P52 子贡欲去告朔之饩羊。子曰："赐也！尔爱其羊，我爱其礼。"

《八佾》第三 — 十七

P53 士志于道，而耻恶衣恶食者，未足与议也。

《里仁》第四 — 九

P54 不患无位，患所以立。不患莫己知，求为可知也。

《里仁》第四 — 十四

P55 见贤思齐焉，见不贤而内自省也。

《里仁》第四 — 十七

P56 父母在，不远游；游必有方。

《里仁》第四 — 十九

P57 德不孤，必有邻。

《里仁》第四 — 二五

P58 子谓子贡曰："女与回也孰愈？"对曰："赐也何敢望回！回也闻一以知十，赐也闻一以知二。"子曰："弗如也，吾与女弗如也。"

《公冶长》第五 — 九

P59 宰予昼寝。子曰："朽木不可雕也，粪土之墙，不可圬也。于予与何诛！"子曰："始吾于人也，听其言而信其行；今吾于人也，听其言而观其行。于予与改是！"

《公冶长》第五 — 一十

P60 子贡问曰："孔文子何以谓之文也？"子曰："敏而好学，不耻下问，是以谓之文也。"

《公冶长》第五 — 十五

P61 巧言、令色、足恭，左丘明耻之，丘亦耻之。匿怨而友其人，左丘明耻之，丘亦耻之。

《公冶长》第五 — 二五

P62 颜渊、季路侍。子曰："盍各言尔志？"子路曰："愿车马、衣轻裘，与朋友共，敝之而无憾。"颜渊曰："愿无伐善，无施劳。"子路曰："愿闻子之志！"子曰："老者安之，朋友信之，少者怀之。"

《公冶长》第五 — 二六

P63 十室之邑，必有忠信如丘者焉，不如丘之好学也。

《公冶长》第五 — 二八

P64 哀公问："弟子孰为好学？"孔子对曰："有颜回者好学，不迁怒，不贰过，不幸短命死矣！今也则亡，未闻好学者也。"

《雍也》第六 — 一二

P65 贤哉回也！一箪食，一瓢饮，在陋巷，人不堪其忧，回也不改其乐。贤哉回也！

《雍也》第六 — 九

P66 知者乐水，仁者乐山。知者动，仁者静。知者乐，仁者寿。

《雍也》第六 — 二一

P67 述而不作，信而好古，窃比于我老彭。

《述而》第七 — 一

P68 默而识之，学而不厌，诲人不倦，何有于我哉？

《述而》第七 — 二

P69 甚矣吾衰也！久矣，吾不复梦见周公！

《述而》第七 — 五

P70 志于道，据于德，依于仁，游于艺。

《述而》第七 — 六

P71 自行束脩以上，吾未尝无诲焉！

《述而》第七 — 七

P72 不愤，不启；不悱，不发。举一隅不以三隅反，则不复也。

《述而》第七 — 八

P73 饭疏食，饮水，曲肱而枕之，乐亦在其中矣。不义而富且贵，于我如浮云。

《述而》篇七 — 十五

P74 我非生而知之者；好古，敏以求之者也。

《述而》第七 — 十九

P75 三人行，必有我师焉。择其善者而从之，其不善者而改之。

《述而》第七 — 二一

P76 子钓而不纲，弋不射宿。

《述而》第七 — 二六

P77 曾子有疾，孟敬子问之。曾子言曰："鸟之将死，其鸣也哀；人之将死，其言也善。君子所贵乎道者三：动容貌，斯远暴慢矣；正颜色，斯近信矣；出辞气，斯远鄙倍矣。笾豆之事，则有司存。"

《泰伯》第八 — 四

P78 学如不及，犹恐失之。

《泰伯》第八 — 十七

P79 逝者如斯夫！不舍昼夜。

《子罕》第九 — 十六

P80 后生可畏，焉知来者之不如今也？四十五十而无闻焉，斯亦不足畏也已！

《子罕》第九 — 二二

P81 知者不惑，仁者不忧，通者不惧。

《子罕》第九 — 二八

P82 厩焚。子退朝，曰："伤人乎？"不问马。

《乡党》第十一 — 十二

P83 季路问事鬼神。子曰："未能事人，焉能事鬼？"曰："敢问死？"曰："未知生，焉知死？"

《先进》第十一 — 十一

P84 子贡问："师与商也孰贤？"子曰："师也过，商也不及。"曰："然则师愈与？"子曰："过犹不及。"

《先进》第十一 — 十五

P85 柴也愚，参也鲁，师也辟，由也喭……回也其庶乎！屡空。赐不受命而货殖焉，亿则屡中。

《先进》第十一 — 十七、十八

P86 颜渊问仁。子曰："克己复礼为仁。一日克己复礼，天下归仁焉。为仁由己，而由人乎哉？"颜渊曰："请问其目？"子曰："非礼勿视，非礼勿听，非礼勿言，非礼勿动。"颜渊曰："回虽不敏，请事斯语矣！"

《颜渊》第十二 — 一

P87 司马牛忧曰："人皆有兄弟，我独亡！"子夏曰："商闻之矣：'死生有命，富贵在天。'君子敬而无失，与人恭而有礼，四海之内，皆兄弟也。君子何患乎无兄弟也？"

《颜渊》第十二 — 五

P88 子贡问政。子曰："足食，足兵，民信之矣。"子贡曰："必不得已而去，于斯三者何先？"曰："去兵。"子贡曰："必不得已而去，于斯二者何先？"曰："去食。自古皆有死，民无信不立。"

《颜渊》第十二 — 七

P89　君子成人之美，不成人之恶；小人反是。

　　　　　　　　　　　　　　　　　　　《颜渊》第十二—十六

P90　曾子曰："君子以文会友；以友辅仁。"

　　　　　　　　　　　　　　　　　　　《颜渊》第十二—二四

P91　苟正其身矣，于从政乎何有？不能正其身，如正人何？

　　　　　　　　　　　　　　　　　　　《子路》第十三—十三

P92　子夏为莒父宰，问政。子曰："无欲速，无见小利。欲速则不达，见小利则大事不成。"

　　　　　　　　　　　　　　　　　　　《子路》第十三—十七

P93　宪问耻。子曰："邦有道，谷；邦无道，谷，耻也。"

　　　　　　　　　　　　　　　　　　　《宪问》第十四—一

P94　子路问成人。子曰："若臧武仲之知，公绰之不欲，卞庄子之勇，冉求之艺；文之以礼乐，亦可以为成人矣！"曰："今之成人者，何必然？见利思义，见危授命，久要不忘平生之言，亦可以为成人矣！"

　　　　　　　　　　　　　　　　　　　《宪问》第十四—十三

P95　其言之不怍，则为之也难！

　　　　　　　　　　　　　　　　　　　《宪问》第十四—二一

P96　君子耻其言而过其行。

　　　　　　　　　　　　　　　　　　　《宪问》第十四—二九

P97　子贡方人。子曰："赐也，贤乎哉？夫我则不暇！"

　　　　　　　　　　　　　　　　　　　《宪问》第十四—三一

P98　骥不称其力，称其德也。

　　　　　　　　　　　　　　　　　　　《宪问》第十四—三五

P99　或曰："以德报怨，何如？"子曰："何以报德？以直报怨，以德报德。"

　　　　　　　　　　　　　　　　　　　《宪问》第十四—三六

P100　子曰："莫我知也夫！"子贡曰："何为其莫知子也？"子曰："不怨天，不尤人，下学而上达。知我者，其天乎！"

　　　　　　　　　　　　　　　　　　　《宪问》第十四—三七

P101　子路宿于石门。晨门曰："奚自？"子路曰："自孔氏。"曰："是知其不可而为之者与？"

《宪问》第十四 — 四一

P102　原壤夷俟。子曰："幼而不孙弟，长而无述焉，老而不死，是为贼！"以杖叩其胫。

《宪问》第十四 — 四六

P103　直哉史鱼！邦有道，如矢；邦无道，如矢。君子哉蘧伯玉！邦有道，则仕；邦无道，则可卷而怀之。

《卫灵公》第十五 — 六

P104　子贡问为仁。子曰："工欲善其事，必先利其器。居是邦也，事其大夫之贤者，友其士之仁者。"

《卫灵公》第十五 — 九

P105　人无远虑，必有近忧。

《卫灵公》第十五 — 十一

P106　子贡问曰："有一言而可以终身行之者乎？"子曰："其恕乎！己所不欲，勿施于人。"

《卫灵公》第十五 — 二三

P107　吾尝终日不食，终夜不寝，以思；无益，不如学也。

《卫灵公》第十五 — 三十

P108　当仁，不让于师。

《卫灵公》第十五 — 三五

P109　君子有三戒：少之时，血气未定，戒之在色；及其壮也，血气方刚，戒之在斗；及其老也，血气既衰，戒之在得。

《季氏》第十六 — 七

P110　君子有九思：视思明，听思聪，色思温，貌思恭，言思忠，事思敬，疑思问，忿思难，见得思义。

《季氏》第十六 — 十

P111　齐景公有马千驷，死之日，民无德而称焉。伯夷、叔齐饿于首阳之下，民到于今称之。其斯之谓与？

《季氏》第十六 — 十二

P112 性相近也，习相远也。

《阳货》第十七 — 二

P113 子曰："由也，女闻六言六蔽矣乎？"对曰："未也。""居！吾语女：好仁不好学，其蔽也愚；好知不好学，其蔽也荡；好信不好学，其蔽也贼；好直不好学，其蔽也绞；好勇不好学，其蔽也乱；好刚不好学，其蔽也狂。"

《阳货》第十七 — 八

P114 色厉而内荏，譬诸小人、其犹穿窬之盗也与！

《阳货》第十七 — 十二

P115 孺悲欲见孔子，孔子辞以疾。将命者出户，取瑟而歌，使之闻之。

《阳货》第十七 — 二十

P116 饱食终日，无所用心，难矣哉！不有博奕者乎？为之犹贤乎已！

《阳货》第十七 — 二二

P117 唯女子与小人为难养也！近之则不孙，远之则怨。

《阳货》第十七 — 二五

P118 年四十而见恶焉，其终也已！

《阳货》第十七 — 二六

P119 微子去之，箕子为之奴，比干谏而死。子曰："殷有三仁焉！"

《微子》第十八 — 一

P120 楚狂接舆，歌而过孔子，曰："凤兮！凤兮！何德之衰？往者不可谏，来者犹可追。已而！已而！今之从政者殆而！"孔子下，欲与之言；趋而辟之，不得与之言。

《微子》第十八 — 五

P121 长沮、桀溺耦而耕。孔子过之，使子路问津焉。长沮曰："夫执舆者为谁？"子路曰："为孔丘。"

《微子》第十八 — 六

P122 曰："是鲁孔丘与？"曰："是也。"曰："是知津矣！"问于桀溺，桀溺曰："子为谁？"曰："为仲由。"曰："是鲁孔丘之徒与？"对曰："然。"

《微子》第十八 — 六

P123 曰："滔滔者，天下皆是也；而谁以易之？且而与其从辟人之士也，岂若从辟世之士哉？"耰而不辍。子路行以告。夫子怃然曰："鸟兽不可与同群，吾非斯人之徒而谁与？天下有道，丘不与易也。"

《微子》第十八 — 六

P124　子贡曰："君子之过也，如日月之食焉；过也，人皆见之；更也，人皆仰之。"

《子张》第十九 — 二一

P125—P138　孔子之所严事：于周则老子；于卫，蘧伯玉；于齐，晏平仲；于楚，老莱子；于郑，子产；于鲁，孟公绰。数称臧文仲、柳下惠、铜鞮伯华、介山子然，孔子皆后之，不并世。

孔子曰："受业身通者七十有七人"，皆异能之士也。德行：颜渊，闵子骞，冉伯牛，仲弓。政事：冉有，季路。言语：宰我，子贡。文学：子游，子夏。师也辟，参也鲁，柴也愚，由也喭，回也屡空。赐不受命而货殖焉，亿则屡中。

颜回者，鲁人也，字子渊。少孔子三十岁。颜渊问仁，孔子曰："克己复礼，天下归仁焉。"

孔子曰："贤哉回也！一箪食，一瓢饮，在陋巷，人不堪其忧，回也不改其乐。""回也如愚；退而省其私，亦足以发，回也不愚。""用之则行，舍之则藏，唯我与尔有是夫！"

回年二十九，发尽白，蚤死。孔子哭之恸，曰："自吾有回，门人益亲。"鲁哀公问："弟子孰为好学？"孔子对曰："有颜回者好学，不迁怒，不贰过。不幸短命死矣，今也则亡。"

闵损字子骞。少孔子十五岁。

孔子曰："孝哉闵子骞！人不间於其父母昆弟之言。"不仕大夫，不食污君之禄。"如有复我者，必在汶上矣。"

闵子骞是孔子的学生，其母死，父更娶，复生二子。后母因虐待闵子骞，其父察知，甚怒，欲逐后母，子骞婉言恳留，父母均受感化，终得相安无事，所以孔子称赞他。

冉雍字仲弓。

仲弓问政，孔子曰："出门如见大宾，使民如承大祭。在邦无怨，在家无怨。"

孔子以仲弓为有德行，曰："雍也可使南面。"

仲弓父，贱人。孔子曰："犁牛之子骍且角，虽欲勿用，山川其舍诸？"

仲由字子路，卞人也。少孔子九岁。子路性鄙，好勇力，志伉直，冠雄鸡，佩豭豚，陵暴孔子。孔子设礼稍诱子路，子路后儒服委质，因门人请为弟子。子路问政，孔子曰："先之，劳之。"请益。曰："无倦。"

孔子曰："片言可以折狱者，其由也与！""由也好勇过我，无所取材。""若由也，不得其死然。""衣敝缊袍与衣狐貉者立而不耻者，其由也与！""由也升堂矣，未入于室也。"

宰予字子我。利口辩辞。既受业，问："三年之丧不已久乎？君子三年不为礼，礼必坏；三年不为乐，乐必崩。旧谷既没，新谷既升，钻燧改火，期可已矣。"子曰："于汝安乎？"曰："安。""汝安则为之。君子居丧，食旨不甘，闻乐不乐，故弗为也。"宰我出，子曰："予之不仁也！子生三年然后免于父母之怀。夫三年之丧，天下之通义也。"

端木赐，卫人，字子贡。少孔子三十一岁。

子贡利口巧辞，孔子常黜其辩。问曰："汝与回也孰愈？"对曰："赐也何敢望回！回也闻一以知十，赐也闻一以知二。"

子贡既已受业，问曰："赐何人也？"孔子曰："汝器也。"曰："何器也？"曰："瑚琏也。"

卜商字子夏，少孔子四十四岁。子夏问："'巧笑倩兮，美目盼兮，素以为绚兮'，何谓也？"子曰："绘事后素。"曰："礼后乎？"孔子曰："商始可与言《诗》已矣。"

子贡问："师与商孰贤？"子曰："师也过，商也不及。""然则师愈与？"曰："过犹不及。"子谓子夏曰："汝为君子儒，无为小人儒。"孔子既没，子夏居西河教授，为魏文侯师。其子死，哭之失明。

澹台灭明，武城人，字子羽。少孔子三十九岁。

状貌甚恶。欲事孔子，孔子以为材薄。既已受业，退而修行，行不由径，非公事不见卿大夫。

南游至江，从弟子三百人，设取予去就，名施乎诸侯。孔子闻之，曰："吾以言取人，失之宰予；以貌取人，失之子羽。"

曾参，南武城人，字子舆。少孔子四十六岁。

孔子以为能通孝道，故授之业。作《孝经》。死于鲁。

有若少孔子四十三岁。有若曰："礼之用，和为贵，先王之道斯为美。小大由之，有所不行；知和而和，不以礼节之，亦不可行也。""信近于义，言可复也；恭近于礼，远耻辱也；因不失其亲，亦可宗也。"

孔子既没，弟子思慕，有若状似孔子，弟子相与共立为师，师之如夫子时也。

南宫括字子容。

问孔子曰："羿善射，奡荡舟，俱不得其死然；禹稷躬稼而有天下？"孔子弗答。容出，孔子曰："君子哉若人！""国有道，不废；国无道，免于刑戮。"三复"白珪之玷"，以其兄之子妻之。

公西赤字子华。少孔子四十二岁。

子华使于齐，冉有为其母请粟。孔子曰："与之釜。"请益，曰："与之庾。"冉子与之粟五秉。孔子曰："赤之适齐也，乘肥马，衣轻裘。吾闻君子周急不继富。"

孙子说·兵学的先知
Sunzi Speaks · The Art of War

孙武的生平
The Life of Sun Wu

孙子名叫武，是春秋时代齐国人，著有《孙子兵法》十三篇。

Sunzi, a man lived in the Spring & Autumn period of acient china, whose given name is Wu. He is said to come form the state of Qi, and is credited with having written the thirteen Chapters of Sunzi's Principles and Tactics of Warfare.

他曾将所著兵法进献给吴王阖闾。
He once presented this book to King Hel of Wu.

好极了！写得太好了。
Fantastic! This is wonderful.

先生所著兵法十三篇我都看过了，可不可以拿来实地操演部队呢？
I have read your book, sir, and I am wondering if you could use it to train a contingent here and now.

当然可以。
Of course I can.

可以用妇女来演练吗？
Could you do it using women?

可以。
Yes.

于是吴王便传旨，找来一百八十名宫女，孙子将她们编成两队，令吴王的两位宠姬分任队长，并令全体持戟。
So the king ordered one hundred eighty palace women into the arena. Sunzi then organized them into two units, with the king's two favorite concubines as leaders. Then heequipped eachperson with theweapon of the times, thedagger-axe.

你们知道胸部、左右手和背面的位置吗？
Do you all know the positions of your heart, left and right hands, and your back?

知道。
Yes.

知道。
Yes.

嘻嘻嘻嘻。
Hee hee hee hee.

哈哈
Ha ha

约束不明，申令不清楚，这是为将者的过错；
When the instructions are not clear, it is the fault of the general;

为人将帅者，既已将各种约束及申令都交代清楚了，可是士兵还不照号令操作，这便是士兵的过错。
But when the general has clearly explained his orders and the soldiers still do not act accordingly, this is the fault of the soldiers.

违令者斩，士卒不可尽杀，队长当受其罪。
Disobeying orders brings the punishment of beheading, and since I can't have all of my soldiers killed, the unit leaders must receive the punishment.

哇！饶命啊！
Ah! Spare me!

呀！
Oh no!

寡人已晓得将军能用兵了。但失去两位宠姬，寡人将食不知味。
Sunzi, I see that you can indeed conduct military operations, but if I lose my two most beloved concubines, I'll lose interest in life itself.

161

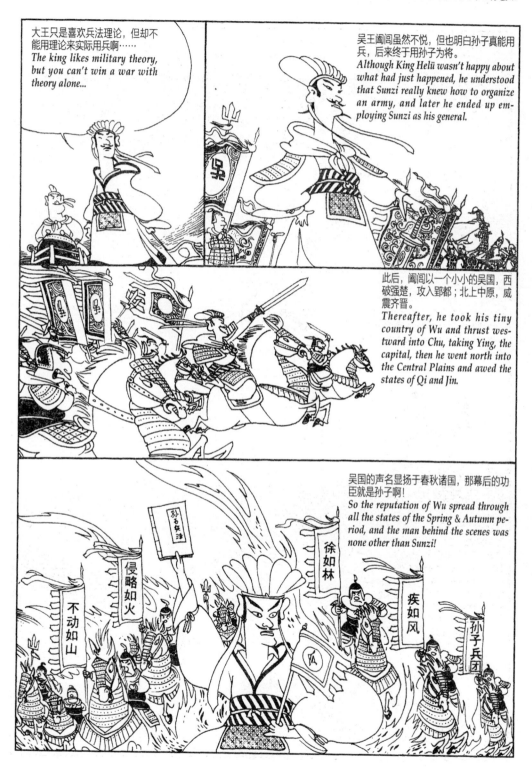

大王只是喜欢兵法理论，但却不能用理论来实际用兵啊……
The king likes military theory, but you can't win a war with theory alone...

吴王阖闾虽然不悦，但也明白孙子真能用兵，后来终于用孙子为将。
Although King Helü wasn't happy about what had just happened, he understood that Sunzi really knew how to organize an army, and later he ended up employing Sunzi as his general.

此后，阖闾以一个小小的吴国，西破强楚，攻入郢都；北上中原，威震齐晋。
Thereafter, he took his tiny country of Wu and thrust westward into Chu, taking Ying, the capital, then he went north into the Central Plains and awed the states of Qi and Jin.

吴国的声名显扬于春秋诸国，那幕后的功臣就是孙子啊！
So the reputation of Wu spread through all the states of the Spring & Autumn period, and the man behind the scenes was none other than Sunzi!

始计篇
Calculation

道、天、地、将、法
The Dao, Heaven, Earth, Command, Law

用兵要从五方面来比较、核算，探求其事实。
We must look at warfare from five different points of view, comparing, calculating, and seeking the facts.

第一是治道；
The first is regulating the Dao, or establishing a moral cause;

第二是天时；
The second is heaven and the seasons, or climate;

第三是地理；
The third is the earth, or terrain and geography;

第四是将领；
The fourth is command, or leadership;

第五是纪律。
The fifth is the law, or discipline.

166

道
The Dao

所谓"治道"，就是要使人民和政府之间具备共同的信念。
Establishing a moral cause means that there must be a common conviction shared by both the people and the government,

全国总动员
Country wide Mobilization

我们为何而战?
Why Are We Going To War

没有国哪有家? 大家同心协力打这场圣战吧!
Without a country, We'd have no home. Let's come together and fight this holy war!

对啊!
Right on!

对啊!
Yes

对啊!
Let's get 'em!

对啊!
Fight!

人民和政府必须同心协力,同生死、共患难而不怕牺牲。
The people must agree with the goals of the government before they will be willing to sacrifice themselves for the sake of the country.

地
Earth

地就是指道途的远近，
"Earth" means distance to be traveled,

地形的险易，地势的广狭，
The traversibility or danger of the terrain, broadness or narrowness of the land,

以及易于逃生或不易于逃生的地形。
And the ease or difficulty of retreating from a certain position.

生地
Safe

死地
Hopeless

绝地
angerous

将
Command

将，是指带兵打仗的将军
必须具备的条件：
"Command" refers to
the characteristics that
a leader of troops must
possess:

才智、威信、仁爱、英勇，
Wisdom, trustworthiness,
benevolence, courage,

及严肃等素养。
And sternness.

法
Law

法，就是指军队的编制、纪律赏罚、军需补给等等。
"Law" means organization of the troops, disciplinary measures of reward and punishment, as well as providing supplies necessary to the army.

法
Law

这几方面的事情，作为军官的都必须深入了解。
Every general must understand these five points.

能正确了解的，便能打胜仗；
If he understands them, he will win;

不能正确了解的，便不能打胜仗。
If he does not understand them, he will not win.

七计
The Seven Calculations

我们要从各方面来比较计算,探求其事实,然后自问……
We must look at warfare from these five points of view, comparing, calculating, and seeking the facts; then we must ask ourselves...

谁的政府能使全体军民同心协力?
Whose government is able to establish a moral cause and gain the whole people's enthusiastic cooperation?

谁的将帅具有才能?
Whose generals are most capable?

谁得天时地利?
Who can take advantage of the benefits of heaven and earth?

谁的法令能贯彻实行?
Whose orders will be carded out most successfully?

173

诡道
Subterfuge

战争是诡诈多端，斗智手段千变万化的行为。
Warfare is deception—the use of clever tactics and movements that are always changing.

有能力，故意装作没有能力；
When you are capable of fighting, make it appear that you are not;

要用兵，故意装作不要用兵；
When you wish to do battle, make it appear that you do not;

Cease Fire, Talk Peace.
休战和谈

哈哈兵力真少
Ha, ha, look how small their camp is.

欲攻近处，故意做出远攻的姿态；
When attacking nearby, make it appear that you are attacking at a distant point;

欲攻远处，故意做出近攻的姿态。
When attacking at a distant point, make it appear that you are attacking nearby.

乘敌
Taking
Advantage
of the
Enemy

或以小利引诱敌人；或在敌人内部制造混乱，再乘乱攻击；敌人充实无弱点时，全力戒备；敌人实力强大时，暂时退避；故意挑逗敌人使其发怒；故示卑弱使敌人松懈；敌人安逸时，设法使其疲于奔命；敌人团结时，设法离间分化。
Lure the enemy with a small advantage;
Sow disorder among the ranks of the enemy, and attack when chaos erupts;
When the enemy exhibits no weak points, fully ready your own side;
When the enemy is strong, avoid him;
Taunt the enemy into anger;
Feign weakness to create overconfidence in the enemy;
When the enemy needs rest, keep him active;
When the enemy is unified, seek to splinter him.

"攻其不备，出其不意"是用兵致胜的秘诀，但战争乃千变万化，必须灵活运用。
Attack when he is unprepared, and appear when unexpected. This is the secret to military success, but because war always changes, you must use it with much versatility.

175

庙算
Temple
Decisions

战争未发生前，先在宗庙里比较敌我双方的优劣。
Before a war has begun, first go to the temple and determime the strong and weak points of each side.

如我方所占的优势多，取胜的机会便大。
If we have more advantages, our chances of winning are greater.

如我方所占的优势少，则得胜的机会便少。
If we have fewer advantages, our chances of winning are smaller.

精详计划，可以打胜仗；不精详地计划，不能打胜仗，何况没有计划呢？
With correct calculations, a war can be won. You cannot win with incorrect calculations, let alone no calculations at all.

我们用这种方法去观察，胜败是可以预知的。
If examined with this in mind, the victor and the vanquished can be predicted.

作战篇
Waging War

日费千金
A Million Dollars a Day

孙子说：就用兵作战的法则而言，要准备一千辆战车及一千辆辎重车辆。

Sunzi said: As for the principles and tactics of warfare, in preparing for war, you will need one thousand chariots and one thousand supply wagons.

配合十万穿着甲胄的战士，自千里之外运送粮食……

These will be accompanied by ten thousand armored soldiers, and food will have to be transported one thousand leagues...

则前后方之军费，外交情报的支出，胶漆器材的补充，车辆甲胄的修护，每天都要用大量金钱，

Add on the expenditures for intelligence reports, supplemental provisions, and maintenance of equipment, and the total will be a great sum of money every day,

然后十万大军才能行动。

And only when all these are prepared can a contingent of one hundred thousand soldiers set out.

久战不利
Protracted War is Disadvantageous

大军出征作战，以争取胜利为第一要务。
When an army goes off to war, victory should be the primary goal.

时间拖延一久，必使军队疲惫，锐气挫失，攻击时战力消耗殆尽。
Once the war drags on, the troops become tired, and their morale suffers. When it comes time to attack, their strength is quickly exhausted.

加以长久用兵在外，必使国家财用不足。
A protracted war will also deplete the funds of the state.

国防经费还差三十万金。
We're still thirty million short for our defense budget.

快回来救援啊！
Hurry back to help out at home!

我这边也走不开呀！
I can't get away right now!

这时，邻近敌国便会乘机入侵；这时虽是有智谋之领导者，也无法善后了。
It is at this time that neighboring states will take advantage of the situation and invade, and even the most clever of leaders will be at a loss to do anything.

贵胜不贵久
Victory Not
Duration

用兵作战，只宜速战速决，不可逞强持久。
In war, you should fight and resolve it quickly. Don't dragit our by showing off your military might.

胜负
Winner Loser

战争拖延持久，对国家毫无益处。
When war is protracted,there is absolutely no benefit to the country.

战争愈持久，则其害愈多且大，虽胜也得不偿失。用兵作战贵胜不贵久，迅速击败敌人，迅速结束战事，以免民劳生怨。长久处于战事，必导致国家经济崩溃。
The longer the war, the more and greater damage done, and even if you win, the gains will not make up for the losses. Aim for victory not duration. By quickly defeating the enemy and resolving the conflict, you will avoid tiring and angering the people and miring your country in war, which would surely lead to a collapse of the economy.

181

高明的将领，务求在敌人的国境补充粮食。
The wise general seeks his grain within the territory of the enemy.

吃敌粮一钟，抵得上自己的二十钟；
To eat one sack of the enemy's grain is to save twenty of your own;

吃敌人二石秆秣草料，就抵得上自己二十石。
To use two bushels of the enemy's fodder is to save twenty of your own.

粮食都被抢光，吃不饱饿着肚子怎么打仗？
Oh no, all the food's been stolen. How can we fight on an empty stomach?

此外，要士卒勇敢杀敌，须激起敌忾之气。
Also, you must instill your soldiers with the courage to destroy the enemy. Thus, you must invoke their hostility.

敌人说我们是群老弱无能之兵，不堪一击。
The enemy said that we're just a bunch of sissies who can't even take a punch.

可恶，与他拼了。
Ooooo, let's get 'em!

要夺取敌人物资，须以财货重赏士卒。
Entice your men to capture the enemy's supplies and equipment by offering rewards.

能夺得车甲物资者，赏黄金十两。
Anyone who captures enemy equipment will be awarded one hundred gold-pieces.

知兵之将
民之司命
The General
Who Knows

速战速决!
Quick to fight,
quick to end it!

因此，用兵作战以求得胜利为首要，绝不能拖延太久。
Military actions should take victory as their main objective, and should never be allowed to go on too long.

一个懂得用兵的将帅，他掌握民族的生命，也是国家安危的主宰。
A general who understands how to fight a war knows that he holds the survival of the people in his hands and is the protector of the country's peace.

善用兵者，要在战场上与战斗中壮大自己，转变敌人力量成为自己的力量，并深知战争持久之害而采战速决之战法。故知兵之将，为国家安危所系!
An able military commander makes his forces appear larger than they are, makes the enemy's strengths his own, has a profound understanding of the dangers of protracted war, and aims at ending a military action as soon as possible. Therefore, the general who understands warfare is the key to peace in a country!

谋攻篇
Strategic Offensive

用兵之法
The Principles of Warfare

孙子说：
Sunzi said:

战争的法则，以保全国家完整为上策，国家受损失，虽然战胜也是差了些。

As for the principles and tactics of warfare, keeping the country whole is better than bringing harm to it, even if victory were to be gained.

保持全军完整为上策，受到损伤就差了些；保持全旅完整为上策，受到损伤就差了些；保持全卒完整为上策，受到损伤就差了些；保持全伍完整为上策，受到损伤就差了些。

Keeping the army whole is better than bringing harm to it;
Keeping a battalion whole is better than bringing harm to it;
Keeping a company whole is better than bringing harm to it;
Keeping a squad whole is better than bringing harm to it.

因此，百战百胜还称不上高明中的高明。
Therefore, fighting and winning a hundred wars is not the greatest good.

能够不必打仗，而能使敌人降服，才是高明中的最高明。
The greatest good is getting the enemy to surrender without ever having to fight.

杀！
Kill!

嘻……不战而胜！
Ha, ha... I won without fighting!

187

政略
Attack
Strategy

最高明的战略是以谋略战胜敌人。
The best plan in war is to attack through the use of cunning strategy.

运用头脑就把敌人打败了!
Use your brain to beat the enemy!

其次是用外交的方式使敌人屈服;
The next best plan is to attack the enemy through alliances, forcing the enemy to capitulate;

再其次就是用强大的军力使敌人屈服;
After that, the best strategy is to attack the enemy using a strong army, thereby forcing him to surrender;

投降!
I surrender!

将帅觉得太慢，不能克制其焦躁忿怒，下令攻击，士兵像蚂蚁一样，爬到城墙上攻城，死伤达三分之一……

If a general feels that this is too slow, and unable to control his fury, he orders the soldiers to attack like so many ants, one third of them will die...

而城池仍攻不下来，那真是攻击作战中，最悲惨的灾祸。

And the wall will remain standing. This is the sad calamity of besieging cities.

190

所以善于用兵的统帅，不经战斗即能屈服敌人；
So an able military commander can get the enemy to surrender without fighting;

输了！
I lose!

降 Surrender

不经攻坚即能取得敌人城池；
Can capture the enemy's city without laying siege to it;

不须长久时间即能摧毁敌国。
And he can destroy the enemy country without engaging in a protracted war.

总之，力量弱小的军队，如不自量力地硬碰……
To conclude, if a small army stubbornly takes on a large army without first considering its own size...

来场硬碰硬的决战，看谁胜谁败。
All fight, let's get it over with fight now!

就必然成为强大敌人的俘虏了。
It will be taken prisoner by the larger army.

投降！
I give up!

当兵力比敌人强时，则可围之、攻之、分之，兵力不若敌人时要能战、能守、能避，并须以优良的指挥，才能达成战、守、避的目的，否则即有惨败被歼灭的危险。
When your forces are stronger than the enemy's, surround him, attack him, and divide him. When your forces don't measure up to the enemy's, be able to fight, be able to hold your ground, and be able to evade him. In addition, there must be exceptional leadership to attain the goals of fighting, holding ground, and evading the enemy, otherwise there will be the danger of suffering an agonizing defeat.

195

统帅权
Powers of the Commander

将帅是国家的支柱。
The general is the pillar of a country.

将帅武德周备，国势必强……
If the general's character and abilities are without reproach, the country will be strong...

如果将帅武德不周，国家必衰弱。
If they are lacking, the country will be weak.

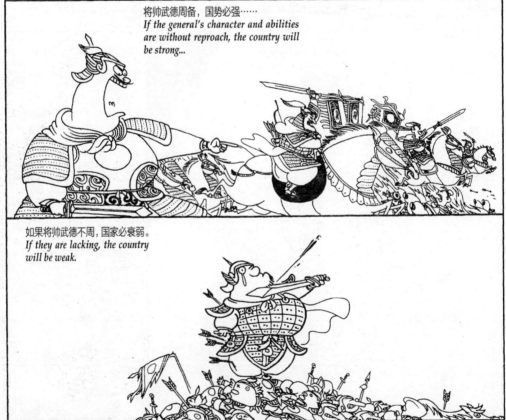

军队如产生疑惧，必使敌国乘隙而来，这就是搅乱自己的军旅导致敌人的胜利。

If confusion or doubt take hold in your army, the enemy will take advantage and advance. So we say, causing havoc in one's own army leads to victory for the enemy.

所以，求得胜有五法：

There are five points that can help calculate which side will be victorious:

一、知道什么情况可以作战或不可作战的能获胜。二、了解这场战役应配置多少兵力的能获胜。三、政府与人民具有共同信念的能获胜。四、自己准备充分，而敌人准备不足的能获胜。五、将帅有才能，而君主不加牵制的能获胜。

1. *They who know when to fight and when not to fight will win.*
2. *They who know how many men to call up for battle will win.*
3. *They who can establish a moral cause between the government and the people will win.*
4. *They who are well-prepared while the enemy is ill-prepared will win.*
5. *They whose general is capable and whose sovereign does not interfere will win.*

这五项是预知胜负的先决条件。

The outcome of a conflict can be predicted according to these five criteria.

军形篇
Tactical Disposition

战略的目的
The
Objective
of Strategy

从前善于用兵作战的人，总是先创造有利形势，使自己不被敌人战胜，然后等待可能战胜敌人的机会。
Prior to war, the great generals of the past would strengthen their own side both morally and materially, and then they would wait for an opportunity to attack the enemy.

我军能否立于不败之地，操之在自己。
Whether or not my army can be defeated depends on me.

敌人有没有犯错误，而使我有得胜机会，却操之在敌人。
Whether or not the enemy makes a mistake that would allow me the opportunity to gain victory depends on him.

所以善于用兵作战的人，能不让敌人有可胜的机会，但不见得使敌人必定为我所胜。
So we see that the great general can protect himself from giving the enemy an opportunity for victory, but he cannot make the enemy susceptible to defeat.

所以说：胜利固然可以预知，但是敌人有无可乘之隙，却不能勉强造成。
Therefore, it is said, victory can be known but not made. In other words, victory can be predicted, but whether or not the enemy gives us an opportunity cannot be forced.

守
Defend

当我无法战胜敌人时，应采取防守方式；
When we cannot defeat the enemy, we should take up a defensive position;

攻
Attack

能战胜敌人时，应采取攻势。
When we can defeat the enemy, we should engage battle.

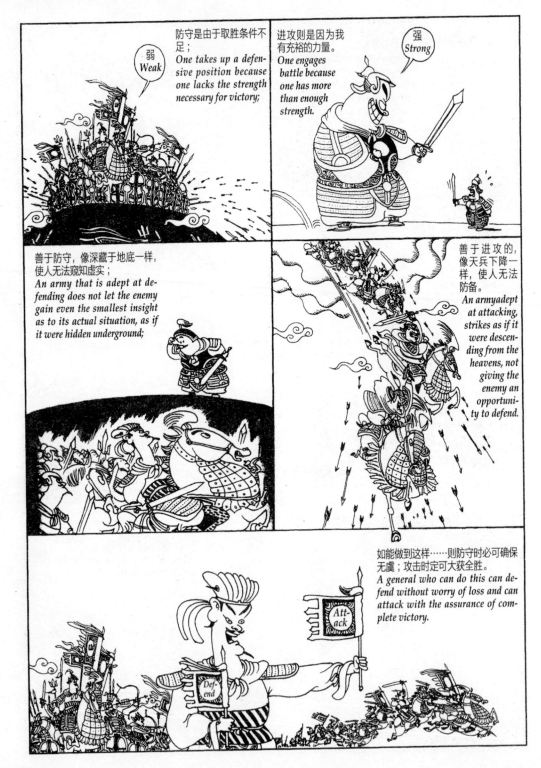

弱
Weak

防守是由于取胜条件不足；
One takes up a defensive position because one lacks the strength necessary for victory;

进攻则是因为我有充裕的力量。
One engages battle because one has more than enough strength.

强
Strong

善于防守，像深藏于地底一样，使人无法窥知虚实；
An army that is adept at defending does not let the enemy gain even the smallest insight as to its actual situation, as if it were hidden underground;

善于进攻的，像天兵下降一样，使人无法防备。
An army adept at attacking, strikes as if it were descending from the heavens, not giving the enemy an opportunity to defend.

如能做到这样……则防守时必可确保无虞；攻击时定可大获全胜。
A general who can do this can defend without worry of loss and can attack with the assurance of complete victory.

Att-ack

Def-end

204

先胜求战
Seek Victory Before Fighting

善用兵作战者，先要站在不失败的基础上，使敌人无机可乘，
The able military commander first stands on a foundation of invincibility, not giving the enemy a single opportunity to take advantage of,

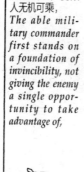

而且不要错过敌人败亡之机会。
And he doesn't miss his chance to defeat the enemy.

所以胜利者都是先创造必胜的条件，然后再与敌人作战。
So we see, the victorious person creates the conditions for certain victory and then does battle with the enemy.

现在已有必胜的把握，冲出去将敌人打败吧！
Now that we are assured victory, strike and defeat the enemy.

杀!
Kill!

善用兵作战者的胜利，既显不出智谋的名声，也看不出勇武的功劳，因为他的取胜都是有把握的，其所以有把握是因为他的措施都已先站在胜利的基础上，自然能胜过那些已经显露出失败征兆的敌人。

As for the victory of an able military commander, he does not reveal his strategy, nor can you see the effort behind his valor. This is because his battle is begun with the confidence of success, and the reason for his confidence is that all of his tactics stand on a foundation of victory. Naturally he can overcome those enemies that have already revealed signs of defeat.

决战的形势
The Cir-
cumstances
of Decisive
Baffle

善于用兵者，修明军政，确保法制，所以能主宰胜败。
The able military commander brings enlightenment to the military administration and upholds regulations. Because of this, he is able to control victory and defeat.

用兵之法是：一、判断战区战线。二、部署计划投入的力量。三、计算所需人力物力的数目。四、比较权衡双方政治及军事力量。五、战胜敌人。
As for the principles and tactics of warfare, there are:
Ⅰ: Measurement—judging the terrain and possible battle lines.
Ⅱ:Appraisal—estimating the necessary kinds of force.
Ⅲ: Calculation—calculating the amount of troops and materials.
Ⅳ:Deliberation—weighing the advantages and disadvantages of the two sides.
Ⅴ: Victory.

根据地形产生作战判断，根据判断产生部署计划，根据部署决定人力物力的数量，根据数量比较权衡，最后得出胜算的结果。
The land dictates the measurement.
The measurement dictates the appraisal.
The appraisal dictates the calculation.
The calculation dictates the deliberation.
And the deliberation dictates the possibility of victory.

战争之胜利者，通常集中一切有形无形的优势军力于决战地点，若以镒称铢，等于四五百倍的悬殊，败者恰好相反，居于绝对的劣势。
The victor concentrates all of his tangible and intangible advantages into the place of decisive battle and is like the weight of a ton compared to the weight of a pound. Conversely, the vanquished is at a distinct disadvantage.

掌握胜利契机的军旅，在作战的时候，像从八千丈高的山涧中，放出的积水一样，势不可当，这就是敌人无从抵抗的形势了。
The victor giving battle is like obstructed water suddenly bursting over the edge of a thousand-foot high chasm. These are the invincible tactical dispositions.

兵势篇
Force

奇、正
Frontal and Sur- prise

管理人数众多的部队，要像管理人数少的部队一样，这是属于编组的问题。
Managing an army with a large contingent of men is the same as managing an army with a small contingent of men. It is merely a question of organization.

指挥大部队作战，如同指挥小部队作战一样，这是属于号令的问题。
Commanding a large army in battle is the same as commanding a small army in battle. It is merely a question of formations and signals.

大军人数众多，要使其一旦受攻击而不失败，这是奇、正互相运用的问题。
A large army must be able to withstand an enemy attack without suffering defeat. This is a question of the effective implementation of frontal and surprise confrontations.

要能像以石击卵一样所向无敌，这是虚实运用的问题。
You should approach the enemy like a stone smashing into an egg. This is a question of the effective implementation of strength and weakness.

奇正之变
The Implementation of Frontal and Surprise Attacks

大凡作战，都是以用兵的正常法则与敌会战。
In wars, you generally use the frontal methods of waging battle with the enemy.

然后顺应战况变化，用奇兵取胜。
And then you adapt to the changing circumstances of the war and use a surprise attack to gain victory.

所以善于出奇制胜的将帅，就像天地那样变化无穷；
A commander who knows how to employ surprise attacks is like heaven and earthinfinite in transformations;

像江河那样奔流不竭；
He is like rivers and streams-flowing endlessly;

211

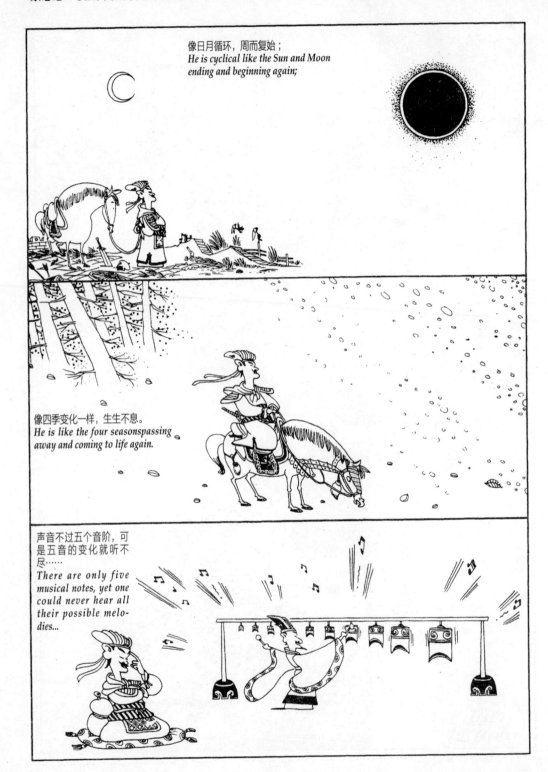

像日月循环，周而复始；
He is cyclical like the Sun and Moon
ending and beginning again;

像四季变化一样，生生不息。
He is like the four seasonspassing
away and coming to life again.

声音不过五个音阶，可
是五音的变化就听不
尽……
There are only five
musical notes, yet one
could never hear all
their possible melo-
dies...

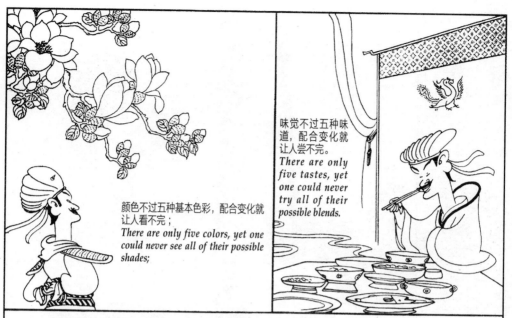

颜色不过五种基本色彩，配合变化就让人看不完；
There are only five colors, yet one could never see all of their possible shades;

味觉不过五种味道，配合变化就让人尝不完。
There are only five tastes, yet one could never try all of their possible blends.

作战的形态不过是奇、正两种，配合变化却是无穷无尽。奇、正互相变化，如同顺着圆环旋转一样，永无止境。
Frontal and surprise confrontations are the only two kinds of force for waging war, yet their possible combinations are limitless. Their mutual transformation is like tracing the line of a circle—there is no endpoint.

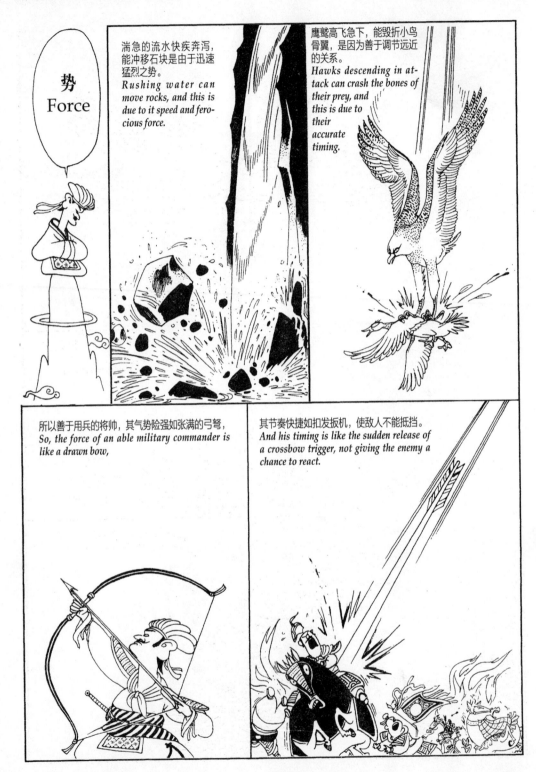

势
Force

湍急的流水快疾奔泻，能冲移石块是由于迅速猛烈之势。
Rushing water can move rocks, and this is due to it speed and ferocious force.

鹰鹫高飞急下，能毁折小鸟骨翼，是因为善于调节远近的关系。
Hawks descending in attack can crash the bones of their prey, and this is due to their accurate timing.

所以善于用兵的将帅，其气势险强如张满的弓弩，
So, the force of an able military commander is like a drawn bow,

其节奏快捷如扣发扳机，使敌人不能抵挡。
And his timing is like the sudden release of a crossbow trigger, not giving the enemy a chance to react.

造势
Creating Force

善用兵作战的将帅，只会在战争态势上寻求胜利，不会苛责部属。
An able military commander seeks victory through force but does not demand it from his men alone.

因而他能选择适当人才，造成战争有利的形势。
Because of this, he can choose men and utilize force.

善任势的将帅，他与敌作战，好像转动圆木与石头一样，圆木石头的特性是放在平坦的地方就静止；
One who utilizes force employs his men as if rolling logs or stones down a hill. It is the nature of logs and stones that on level ground they remain still;

放在陡斜的地方就滚动！
While on a slope, they move.

所以高明的将帅造就之势，如同把圆木石头从千丈高山滚下来一样，
So the force that a commander creates is like a round log or rock plunging downward from a thousand feet up,

其势凶猛不可当，这就是军事上所谓的"势"。
And its ferocity is unstoppable. This is what is meant by force.

虚实篇
Strength and Weakness

致人而不致于人
Control Others Without Being Controlled

凡先到达战地等待敌人的，就居于从容主动地位；
Whoever arrives at the battlefield first will be at ease and in a position to take the initiative;

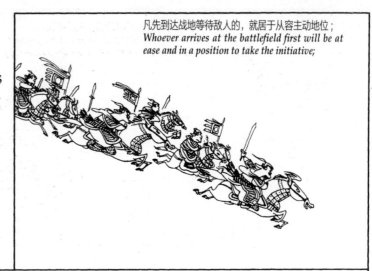

后到达战地而仓促应战的，就居于疲劳被动地位。
The latecomer will have to rush to meet the enemy on the battlefield and thus will be tired and at a disadvantage.

所以善于用兵作战者，总是支配敌人，而不被敌人支配。
The able military commander controls the enemy and is not controlled by the enemy.

过来过来！过来呀！
Come on!
Come On!

嘻嘻
Hee... Hee..

要使敌人来我预定之决战地点，应以利引诱；
One who wants to get the enemy to his choice of battlefields entices him with an apparent advantage;

要使敌人不敢来，必设治防害之，叫他不敢来。
One who wants to keep the enemy away threatens him with force.

所以敌欲休息，则设治使之疲于奔命；敌欲温饱，则设治使他饥饿；敌如安处不动，则设治使其移动，俾中我计。
When the enemy wants rest, keep him running; when he is idle, make him move.

我专敌分
Concentration Against Frag-mentation

虚张声势，使敌人莫测我之虚实，则能做到我兵力集中，而敌人的兵力分散。

By employing diversionary tactics and keeping your real circumstances hidden, you can fool the enemy in regard to your actual size and location, thereby forcing the enemy to spread out. In this way, the enemy's forces will be divided, while your own are still concentrated.

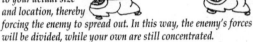

主力在这里。
Here's my main force!

我之兵力集中一处，敌人的兵力分散十处，这样就能以十倍的力量打击敌人。
I concentrate my power in one place, while the enemy's is fragmented in ten places. This way, I have a tenfold advantage.

以人数多攻击人数少，则与我交战之对象就弱小易制了。
By outnumbering the enemy, he is rendered weak and easy to control.

力量被分散了，打不赢他了……
I can't win with this fragmenta-tion...

"我专敌分"乃是在一定时间、空间内，将最大战力置于决胜点上，对敌实行决定性打击，而发挥绝对的优势。

At a specified time and in a specified place, concentration against fragmentation is exerting the greatest power at a point of certain victory, thus striking a decisive blow against the enemy and giving you certam supenriority.

兵形如水
Like Water

用兵的规律应像水一样，水是由高往低处流。
The principle for deploying soldiers is to emulate water. Water flows from higher ground to lower ground.

用兵的规律是避实而击虚。
And the role for waging war is to avoid strengths and strike at weaknesses.

水因地形而变化其方向；
Water changes course according to terrain;

用兵也要顺应敌情变化而克敌制胜。
And in military deployment, you want to change your course toward victory according to the enemy's changing circumstances, confronting him and defeating him.

221

所以用兵没有固定的规则，就像水没有固定的形态一样，能依照敌情变化而取胜，才算是用兵如神了。
There are no absolute precepts for waging war, just like water does not have only one shape. He is indeed a god-like general who can adapt with the changing conditions of a war and thereby gain victory.

用兵如同"五行"变化一样——金木水火土相生相克，不分谁胜。
Deploying forces is like the transformations among the five elements—metal, wood, water, fire, and earth—alternately arising and giving way, not concerned with which one is at a temporary advantage.

春夏秋冬，交替更迭。
Spring, summer, fall, and winter take turns one after the other;

日有长有短；
Some days are long and others short;

月有圆有缺。
The moon waxes and wanes.

用兵之道，没有一定的法则，就像水一样，因地形而改变其流向，故用兵无常形，避实击虚，随时依敌情变化，而变化我之奇正。
The principle of deploying forces is that there are no certain methods, just like flowing water, which is constantly changing direction. So there are no certain rules for military deployment—just avoid strengths and strike at weaknesses. Alternate your tactics from surprise to frontal and back, according to the enemy's circumstances.

223

军争篇
Maneuver

以迂为直
Make the
Crooked
Straight

大凡用兵的法则，是到前线与敌军争夺有利的制胜条件。
The correct method of manipulating forces is to struggle with the enemy at the front lines for advantages that can lead to victory.

如何化种种不利为有利。
How to turn all kinds of disadvantages into advantages.

如何化迂回曲折之远路为直线近路，比敌军先赶到战场。
How to turn the long distance of a crooked road into the short distance of a straight road, thereby arriving at the battlefield before the enemy.

在互相争取有利的制胜条件中，既有其有利的一面，也有其危险的一面。
When straggling for advantages that can lead to victory, there are beneficial aspects as well as dangerous aspects.

嘻嘻嘻……
Hee, hee,hee...

225

利与弊
Advantage
and Disad-
vantage

全军人马辎重一同行动，则必定迟缓。
If the entire army sets out together, with men, horses, and carts, the going will surely be slow.

可是若将辎重装备留置后方，行动虽快，但有时会被敌人夺去。
And although it would be swifter if the carts and equipment were left behind, they could easily be captured by the enemy.

哈哈哈，夺到敌人的后勤补给装备，这场战争我赢定了。
Ha, ha, ha. Now that we have the enemy's supplies, we'll win for sure.

哇
Ah!

况且，轻装急行、昼夜不息，虽可加倍速度日行百里，
Furthermore, if you attempt to make up time by marching all day and all night, you may be able to increase your distance by one hundred leagues a day,

但队伍必定散乱，因为部队中强劲者先到，疲惫者落后，只有十分之一人马能赶到战场。

But the army will be dispersed because the more fleet ones will get out ahead while the slower ones fall behind. If this is the case, only one tenth of your army will be able to make a hasty arrival at the battlefield.

仓促应战，必致失败，三军将帅都有被俘的可能。

And once they arrive there, they will surely be defeated. There is also the possibility that in the defeat, the commanders will be captured.

所以军中没有后勤辎重，不能生存；

Therefore, if it is not backed up by supply wagons, the army will not survive;

没有粮食补给，不能生存；没有装备存储，不能生存。

If there are no supplies and provisions, the army will not survive; if there is no store of equipment, the army will not survive.

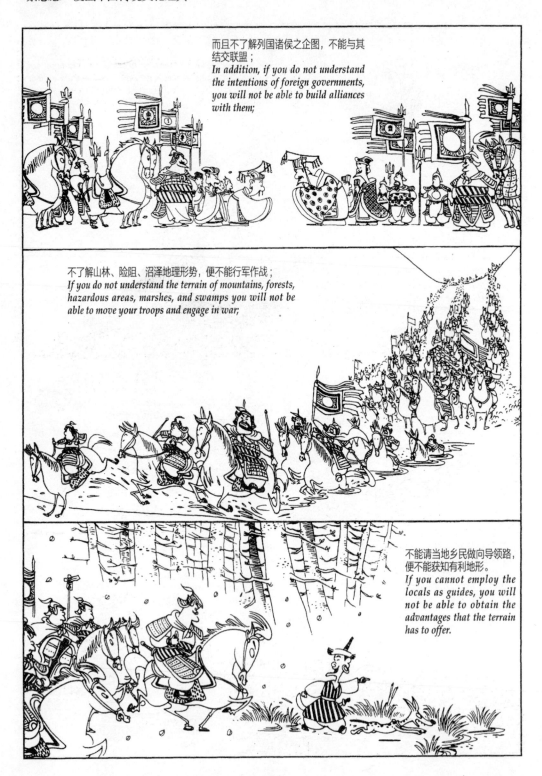

而且不了解列国诸侯之企图，不能与其结交联盟；
In addition, if you do not understand the intentions of foreign governments, you will not be able to build alliances with them;

不了解山林、险阻、沼泽地理形势，便不能行军作战；
If you do not understand the terrain of mountains, forests, hazardous areas, marshes, and swamps you will not be able to move your troops and engage in war;

不能请当地乡民做向导领路，便不能获知有利地形。
If you cannot employ the locals as guides, you will not be able to obtain the advantages that the terrain has to offer.

风林火山
Wind, Forest, Fire, Mountain

用兵作战要奇诡多变才能成功；
When waging war, you must employ cunning tactics and multiple transformations in order to succeed;

要判断是否有利才采取行动；
You must judge whether or not something is advantageous before you act;

要依情况变化而决定兵力之分散或集中。
You must decide whether to concentrate your troops or divide them according to changing circumstances.

风
WIND

军旅行动时，要快如疾风迅速
而无迹；
*When moving, you must be
fleet like the wind;*

静止时，肃穆严整如林木一般；
*When stopping, you must be
still like the trees in a forest;*
林
FOREST

火
FIRE

攻击时，如燎原烈火；
*When attacking, you
must be ferocious
like the searing fla-
mes of a fire;*

山
MOUNTAIN

防守时，如山岳一样不可动摇；
When defending, you must be immovable like a mountain;

雷霆
LIGHTNING

快速行动时，迅如雷电，使敌人无从退避。
When advancing, you must be sudden like lightning, allowing the enemy no chance for retreat.

用兵要根据敌情变化，权衡情势，相机而动，因敌制胜。能确实做到风、林、火、山、阴、雷霆的境界，便易获胜。
When engaging in warfare, you should base your actions on the changing circumstances of the enemy. Consider the changes, take advantage of opportunities, and gain victory through the enemy. If you can be like these six things wind, forest, fire, mountain, cloud, and lightning victory will be yours.

阴
CLOUDS

隐蔽时，匿形敛迹如乌云遮天，使敌人无从知晓；
When hiding, you must completely disappear, as though behind dark clouds;

231

九变篇
Alternatives

九变
Alternatives

孙子说：
Sunzi said:

大凡用兵的法则是，将帅受命于国君，征集民众，组成军旅……
In commanding troops, the general receives the order from the sovereign, the people are conscripted, and an army is formed...

在难以通行之地，不可宿营；
Do not bivouac on hazardous terrain;

在四通八达之地，要注意与邻国结交；
At intersecting territories, ally with the neighboring countries;

在交通不便、补给困难之地，不可滞留；
Do not linger in terrain that separates you from your supplies;

在四面地形险阻之地，易为敌所困，
要速谋逃脱；
In enclosed ground, seek escape;

在后退无路的死地，要拼力死战；
In desperate ground, fight;

虽属应当经过的途径，但为达"以迂为直"
的目的，有的道路不要通过；
Some roads are not to be traversed;

虽遇到必可打败的敌人，但为集中兵力
于其他方面而不击之；
Some armies are not to be engaged;

放过他们，让他们走
吧。
*Let them go. We'll
concentrate our
attack elsewhere.*

虽为必攻的城池，但为有效奸灭敌人而不攻之；
Some cities are not to be stormed;

绕过这座城，直接攻打他们的大本营！
We'll skip the city and directly attack their major encampment.

虽为必争之地，但为速决全胜而不争之；
Some battle-fields are to be foregone;

放弃那边，全力攻打这边！
We'll skip that area and strike here with all our strength!

将在外，君命有所不受。
If your orders are contrary to ultimate victory, I am forced to disobey.

国君的命令，若不利于战争，也可以不接受。
Some of the sovereign's orders are to be ignored.

所以为将帅的，能运用这九种权变而得其益处，就可算是懂得用兵了。
If a commander takes into account the benefits of these alternatives, then he can be said to understand warfare.

不懂得九变之利者，虽知地形，不能得地之利。治理军队如不明了各种权变，虽然知道地形利用的效果，但是不能发挥军旅的效用。
If he does not, then even though he may understand terrain, he will not be able to take advantage of it. If in managing his forces he cannot adjust to changing situations, even though he may understand the benefits to be gained through terrain, he will not be able to fully utilize his forces.

明智的将帅在考虑问题时，必须同时兼顾有利与有害两方面。
When considering problems, the wise general will take into account both the possible benefits and harms.

在不利的状况中，考虑有利的一面，可以增强信念；在有利的状况中，考虑有害的一面，可以解除隐患。
In a disadvantageous situation, considering the possible benefits will increase conviction. In an advantageous situation, considering the possible harm will allow you to avoid hidden danger.

因此，用诸侯害怕的事，使其屈服于我；
Therefore, make noblemen of other countries submit by threatening them;

用种种方式，使诸侯纷乱，内顾不暇；
Make them focus on domestic affairs by inciting internal dissent;

再以利益去引诱，使诸侯归附于我。
Gain their allegiance by enticing them with benefits.

用兵的法则是，不要寄望于敌人不会来，而要依靠自己有万全的准备，严阵以待。
Therefore, according to the principles and tactics of warfare, do not expect the enemy not to come. Instead, be in complete military readiness.

不要寄望于敌人不会进攻，而要靠自己有敌人无法攻破的力量。
Do not expect the enemy not to attack. Instead, assure yourself that the enemy would not be successful in the event of an attack.

将帅有五项最危险的事：
There are five personal traits that are dangerous in a commander:

必死可杀，必生可虏，忿速可侮，廉洁可辱，爱民可烦。
He who is intent on killing can be murdered.
He who is intent on living can be captured.
He who is quick to anger can be insulted.
He who is self-conscious can be humiliated.
He who is compassionate can be troubled.

一、只知死拼，就可能遭敌所杀；
I . He who understands only attack and killing is likely to be cut down by the enemy;

二、贪生怕死，临阵畏怯，就可能遭敌俘虏；
II . He who fears death and is afraid in the face of battle is likely to be captured by the enemy;

行军篇
On the March

部署
Deployment

孙子说：凡军旅部署作战和观察判断敌情，应该注意以下几点：
Sunzi said: When deploying troops and observing the enemy, you should take into account the following points:

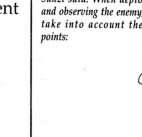

在越山而行时，要沿谷地前进；
When traversing mountains, follow the valley floors;

要注意可攻可守之地，以及可部署之高地；
Look for places suitable to attack or defend, as well as high places that are suitable for stationing troops;

如敌人先占据高地，切勿作正面之仰攻；这是在山地作战时的部署原则。
If the enemy is the first to gain the high ground, do not commence a frontal assault. These are the principles of deploying troops in a mountainous area.

横渡河川后，必迅速远离河岸，以免为敌所乘；
When fording a river, cross quickly and distance yourself from it, lest the enemy take advantage of the situation;

敌人如渡河来攻，切勿迎击于水中。
If the enemy crosses a river in the course of their attack, do not enter the water to engage them.

慢……
Not yet...

等其一半已上岸，一半尚在水中时，发动攻击才有效。
Wait until they are half across and half in the water, then attack.

攻击!
Attack!

如果要与敌军决战，不要沿河岸配置兵力迎战，
If anticipating engagement with the enemy, do not meet them while following a river,

优
Superior

而要在河岸的高地部署兵力。
Rather, ready your forces on high ground facing the water.

劣
Inferior

更不要逆着水流，在敌军下游布阵，这是在河川地区的作战原则。
Even more important, do not take up a position down river from the enemy. These are the principles of deploying troops near rivers.

横越沼泽地区，应迅速离开不要停留；
When crossing through a swamp, do so quickly and do not linger;

如在沼泽地区作战，一定要占水草茂盛之地；
If you must fight in a swamp, stand the ground with the most vegetation;

最好背依树林，这是沼泽地区作战部署原则。
And have your back to a wooded area. These are the principles for deploying troops in a swampy area.

243

如在平原作战，应在地势平坦之处部署。
When waging war on a plain, deploy your troops on level ground.

右翼或背依高地，以地形前低后高为好，这是平原作战之要领。
Have your back or right flank toward high ground. You want the high ground behind you and the low ground before you. These are the principles for deploying troops on a plain.

以上四种作战部署之原则，是远自黄帝时代就遵循的。
The preceding are the principles for deploying troops in the four kinds of terrain. They have been heeded since the times of the Yellow Emperor.

山地作战
河川作战
沼泽作战
平原作战
*Mountain Warfare
River Warfare
Swamp Warfare
Plains Warfare*

其所以能战胜四方，都是依照这些原则。
And the reason he was able to conquer the whole land is that he followed these principles.

> 敌军距我很近而能保持镇静，是依仗其有险要地形。
> *When the enemy is near but calm, he is depending on the hazards of the terrain.*

> 敌军距我很远而又前来挑战，是企图诱我前进。
> *When the enemy charges while still far away, he is enticing me to advance.*

有种杀过来吧！
Come and get me if you can!

哒！哒！
Kalop! Kalop!

> 敌军不居险要，而在平坦之处部署，必有其自以为有利之处。
> *When the enemy takes up a position on level, open ground, there is surely some other benefit for him there.*

245

林中有很多树木摇动，是有敌人来。
The shaking of trees indicates that the enemy is advancing.

在杂草丛生处，设有许多障蔽物，是敌人故布疑阵。
Obstacles in the undergrowth indicate that the enemy suspects our attack.

见鸟雀突然飞起，是有敌人埋伏。
Many birds taking to wing indicate that the enemy is lying in ambush.

见兽类奔逃，是有敌人来袭。
The fleeing of wild animals indicates that the enemy is approaching.

至于尘土，如高扬而且呈尖形，是兵车前来。
In regard to dust, if it rises in a sharp upward column, chariots are approaching.

如低扬而面积广者，是兵卒前来。
If it is low and expansive, infantry are approaching.

如敌方的使者言辞谦卑，但军旅却积极备战，这是向我军进击的预兆。
If the words of the enemy are humble, yet he maintains his readiness, this is a sign that he will attack.

敌方的使者如言辞强硬，并且在行动上摆出进迫之势，这是敌军后退的预兆。
If the enemy's words are forceful and his troops feign advances, this is a sign that he will retreat.

敌军如先派出战车占住两侧，是准备列阵和我决战。
If the enemy advances with chariots on both flanks, he is ready to engage us.

没有提出保证或和约，仅口头言和，则敌人必有计谋。
If the enemy offers peace guarantees or a treaty, he is certain to have ulterior motives.

地形篇
Terrain

249

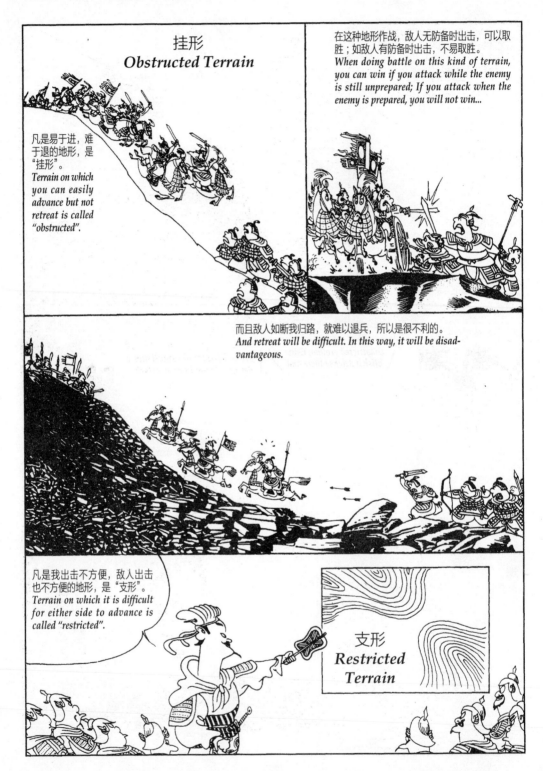

挂形
Obstructed Terrain

凡是易于进，难于退的地形，是"挂形"。
Terrain on which you can easily advance but not retreat is called "obstructed".

在这种地形作战，敌人无防备时出击，可以取胜；如敌人有防备时出击，不易取胜。
When doing battle on this kind of terrain, you can win if you attack while the enemy is still unprepared; If you attack when the enemy is prepared, you will not win...

而且敌人如断我归路，就难以退兵，所以是很不利的。
And retreat will be difficult. In this way, it will be disadvantageous.

凡是我出击不方便，敌人出击也不方便的地形，是"支形"。
Terrain on which it is difficult for either side to advance is called "restricted".

支形
Restricted Terrain

这种地形，敌人尽管引诱我，我也不能出击，可以带兵退去，使敌人来追……
On this kind of terrain, even if the enemy entices you, do not advance. Instead, retreat, forcing him to follow...

等敌军有半数进入这种地形时，再回头攻击，才会形成有利的局面。
Wait until half of them are through, then turn and attack. In this way, it will be advantageous.

至于"隘形"地，我应该设法先占据，守住隘口制敌。
Be the first to stand the constricted ground. Establish a defense there and await the enemy.

如果敌人先占据隘口，而且在隘口布置设防，绝不能强行通过。
If he takes the constricted ground first and establishes a defense, do not force an attack.

隘形
Constricted Terrain

如敌人虽占据隘地，但没有在隘口设防，就可以考虑进击。
If he takes the constricted ground and does not establish a defense, you may consider attacking.

251

险形是重要险关要口，应先期占领，并依据其制高点，以等待敌人。

On precipitous terrain, first stand the essential points of transit and take the high ground, where you will await the enemy.

如敌人先占有时，当即引军他去，千万不可妄行攻击之。

If the enemy gets to these places first, lure him away by leaving. Do not recklessly attack.

险形
Precipitous Terrain

快撤！
Turn back!

远形是敌我相距甚远，此时若势均力敌，兵力相等，双方都难以排阵，更难取胜。

"Distant" terrain refers to both sides being far away from each other. On this kind of terrain, if the forces are equal, it is difficult for either side to win decisively.

以上这六种，是地形利用的原则，也是主帅的首要职责，不能不仔细体察。

These are the six kinds of terrain and the principles for using them correctly. Every responsible general will take them into account.

远形
Distant Terrain

六败
The Six Kinds of Defeat

用兵作战，有走、弛、陷、崩、乱、北六种情况。
In warfare, there are six kinds of disasters that are not due to nature, but are the fault of the commander.

这不是地形的灾害，乃是人为的错误，也就是将领的过失。
They are: haste, laxity, downfall, collapse, chaos, and defeat.

敌我兵力相等，可是不能集中兵力于决战方面，反而以我的一，打敌人的十，叫做"走"。
When forces are equal, and instead of concentrating your men in a decisive attack, you advance with a ratio of one to ten, this is called "haste".

自找死路！
He's committing suicide!

你们攻去，我先走。
You guys go ahead and attack. I'll be right back...

军队装备训练都好，可是指挥官能力薄弱，叫作"弛"。
When the soldiers are well-equipped and well-trained but their officers are weak and unskilled, this is called "laxity".

进攻！
Attack!

指挥官优越，部队士兵差，叫做"陷"。
When the general is skilled and strong but the troops are weak and incompetent, this is called certain "downfall".

可是我们害怕呀！
But we're afraid!

高级军官骄横，遇敌妄动，将帅又无法控制之，叫做"崩"。
When the high-ranking officers dominate and recklessly attack, with the commander unable to control them, this is called "collapse".

不可进攻！
Do not attack!

我才不像你这么怕死呢！
I'm no coward like you are!

集合！
Fall in!

将领约束不严，教导无方，官兵没有纪律，作战部署混乱，叫作"乱"。
If the commander is not strict, is not skilled in training his troops, the troops have no discipline, and battle and deployment are disorganized, this is called "chaos".

管他的。
Take a hike.

将领料敌无方，以寡战众，以弱对强，用兵又无重点，叫做"北"。
If the commander underestimates the enemy, setting a small force against a larger or a weak force against a stronger, or if he does not employ shock troops in the front ranks, this is called certain "defeat".

这六种败亡的原因，都是将领的责任，不可不详细究察之。
To avoid these six kinds of defeat is the responsibility of the commander. Therefore, he must carefully take them into account.

都是我的错才失败了！
It's all my fault that we were defeated!

上将者国之宝
A Great General is a National Treasure

地形是辅助用兵作战的重要条件，能利用地形克敌，则战争必胜，否则必败。
Terrain is an important factor that can be of help in waging war. If you can use it against the enemy, you are assured victory, and if you cannot, defeat is certain.

战必胜，全面进攻！
Victory is certain! All forces attack!

有必胜把握，即当坚定进行到底。反之，则应断然中止作战。
If a general is certain of victory, he should relentlessly attack until victory is gained. If not, he should discontinue waging war.

国家元首的命令，都可暂时不必顾虑。
The general may temporarily disregard the sovereign's orders.

非战不可！
We must fight!

战必败不可战！
If defeat is certain, we should not fight!

为将者，能进而不求名，退而不避罪，完全以国家民族利益为重，才不愧为国家之宝。
The great general advances without seeking recognition and retreats without shirking responsibility He acts only for the benefit of the people. In this way, he is a national treasure.

能不求名不避罪，惟民是保的将领，才是最好的将领。
The best kind of general is one who does not seek fame or avoid blame and who takes the protection of the people as his highest priority.

九地篇
Ground

地略
Strategies
of Ground

根据用兵的原则，有散地、轻地、争地、交地、衢地、重地、圮地、围地、死地九类。
According to the principles and tactics of warfare, there are nine kinds of ground: dispersive, shallow, contentious, communicating pivotal, deep, hazardous, encircled, and mortal.

我军在自己的领土内作战，叫作"散地"。
If your army is battling in your own territory, this is called "dispersive ground".

进入敌境不深的地区，叫作"轻地"。
If you enter a short distance across the border, this is called "shallow ground".

敌我得之均有利的兵家必争之地，叫作"争地"。
When we have both gained the same advantageous position, this is called "contentious ground".

我军可以往，敌军也可以来的地区，叫作"交地"。
When I can advance toward the enemy and the enemy can advance toward me, this is called "communicating ground".

占领之，可以控制邻近各国的军事行动者，叫作"衢地"。
When you have occupied a strategic area from which you can control the other states, this is called "pivotal ground".

深入敌国境内，已经过许多城邑者，叫作"重地"。
When you are far inside the enemy's territory and have passed several towns and cities, this is called "deep ground".

进入的途径狭隘，退回的道路迂远，敌人可以寡击我之众的地方，叫作"围地"。
When you enter a passageway that is narrow, where the road of retreat is long or where you can be attacked from all sides, this is called "encircled ground".

山岳、森林、险要、沼泽等难于通行的地方，叫作"圮地"。
When you are in the mountains, a forest, on dangerous terrain, or in a swamp or marsh, this is called "hazardous ground".

迅速决战就可以生存，否则有败亡可能的地区，叫作"死地"。
When you have no choice but to fight or die, this is called "mortal ground".

258

所以在"散地"，不宜早期决战，当诱敌深入，再予重击；
On dispersive ground, do not engage the enemy right away. Before attacking, entice the enemy deeper into your own territory;

在"轻地"不宜停止，应继续进军；
On shallow ground, you should not hold back, but continue fighting on;

遇"争地"应事先占领，不可等敌人占领后，再进攻；
In regard to contentious ground, you must occupy it first. If the enemy occupies it, do not attack;

逢"交地"也应先占领，以阻止敌人，并确保我军后方联络线；
When on communicating ground, be sure and maintain your lines of supply and information;

在"衢地"则应交结邻邦；
When you are on pivotal ground, you are free to begin diplomatic negotiations;

在"重地"应就地补给；
When on deep ground, plunder for provisions;

快走！这里最忌遭伏击！
Let's go! This is where we are most vulnerable!

在"圮地"应迅速离去；
When on hazardous ground, make haste to get out of it;

在"围地"应用计谋脱困；
When on encircled ground, devise a strategy to free yourself;

在"死地"应奋力死战。
When on mortal ground, fight tooth and nail.

内线作战
Fighting on Internal Lines

自古以来,善用兵作战者,能使敌人前后无法顾及。
Ever since ancient times, an able military commander kept the enemy from protecting both his front and rear.

大部队和小部队之间无法联系,各自为战,不能相互救援。
He would cut off the smaller forces from the larger, so that they would be isolated and could not come to each other's aid.

也无法收兵转移,士卒溃散不集中,主力未能齐一,即行攻击。
He would keep them from changing position or concentrating their strength in attack.

总之,有利才行动,无利则不妄动。
Only act when in an advantageous position; and when in a disadvantageous position, don't do anything rash.

261

霸王之兵
The Army of the Supreme Sovereign

不了解国际情势者，不能运用外交。
One who does not understand international affairs will not be able to effectively make use of diplomatic relations.

抱歉！我国的政策已改，对不起……
Sorry, but our country's policy has suddenly changed. My apologies...

不熟悉山林险要沼泽地理者，不能行军作战。
One who is not familiar with the geography of mountains, forests, swamps, marshes, and other hazardous terrain will not be able to lead troops into battle.

不重用战地乡民做向导者，不能得地形地略的利用。
One who does not utilize the locals as guides will not be able to use the terrain to his advantage.

这三项缺一，就不能算是霸王的军旅。
If a general lacks one of the above characteristics, his army cannot be called the army of the supreme sovereign.

用兵如常
山之蛇
**Wage War
Like a Serpent**

善于用兵者，就像"率然"一样，
"率然"是常山的蛇……
An able military commander is like the shuairan snake of Mount Chang...

打它头部，尾部就来救应；
If you attack its head, its tail strikes;

打它尾部，头部就来救应；
If you attack its tail, its head strikes;

打它中间，头尾一同来救。
If you attack its middle, both its head and tail strike.

用兵可以像这种蛇一样吗？
Can an army fight like this?

可以。
Certainly.

例如吴人和越人交恶……
For instance, suppose there were two men, one from Wu and one from Yue, who were enemies...

但若他们同乘一船而遇风浪时，也能如左右手一样互相救援。
Now, if they happened to be on the same boat in the event of a terrible storm, they would become like the left and right hands of the same person, helping each other out of difficulty.

所以把马匹缚在一起，把车轮埋起来，强行使其动作一致，是靠不住的。
So, even stringing the horses together, burying the chariot wheels in the dirt, and forcing the soldiers to march in unison cannot be counted on to create cooperation among the soldiers.

要使士卒勇敢齐一，有赖指挥得法，使强者与弱者各尽其力，
You must encourage the soldiers to fight with bravery and unity, give them the discipline to follow commands, and make both the strong and weak give their all,

而且还要明了地理形势并加以利用。
You must also understand geographical conditions and use them to your advantage.

善于用兵者，指挥大军就像指挥一个人一样容易……
For an able military commander, directing the operations of an entire army is like directing the actions of one person...

拼了。
The fight is on.

没有后路了……
We can't move back...

因为他把士兵放在不得已的境地，使他们非战不可。
Because he puts the soldiers in a situation where they are forced to fight.

良好的将领统率百万大军，能使万众齐勇一心，生死与共互相救援。因为他先将军队置于"死地"，士卒后无退路，不战则亡，所以非力拼不可。
The great commander of a large force is able to rally his soldiers to act with one mind, fighting to the death or helping each other out of trouble. He does this by placing them on "mortal ground", thus giving them no choice but to fight or die.

始如处女，敌人开户，后如脱兔，敌不及拒
Like a Maiden

军事行动开始时，像处女一样沉静，让敌人放松戒备；
At the beginning of a war, you should be quiet and reserved like a young maiden. In this way, the enemy will relax and lower his defenses;

像个黄花大闺女一样！
Hey you sissies!

没经验啊！
No experience!

嘻嘻嘻
Hee, hee, hee...

然后像脱兔一样迅速，使敌人抗拒不及，取得胜利。
Then you spring like a jack-rabbit. The enemy won't have time to react, and victory is yours.

火攻篇
Incendiary Warfare

火攻有五
The Five Methods of Incendiary Warfare

用火攻敌有五种方式：一是火烧杀敌军士卒；二是火烧敌军堆积之粮秣；三是火烧敌军之辎重运输；四是火烧敌军之仓库储藏；五是火烧敌军大队人马。
There are five methods of attacking the enemy with fire: -Set fire directly to the enemy soldiers. -Set fire to the enemy's stockpile of grain. -Set fire to the enemy's supply wagons. -Set fire to the enemy's stores of provisions. -Set fire to the enemy's main contingent of men and horses.

发动施行火攻必须具备一定的条件，同时引火的工具也要经常准备。
There must be the right criteria to initiate an incendiary attack, and one must already have the right equipment at hand.

发动火攻要乘有利时机，引燃火势也须选择有利的日子。
When attacking with fire, you must do so at an advantageous time on an advantageous day.

所谓时机是指天气干燥，久旱不雨；
"At an advantageous time" means that the weather must be dry and the place in question must have gone without rain for a period of time.

所谓有利的日子是指月亮运行到箕、壁、翼、轸四个星宿时，就是起风的日子。
"On an advantageous day" means a day when the moon is found in the constellation of Sagittarius, Pegasus, Crater, or Corvus, which will be a day of rising wind；

合于利而动
Move Only When It Benefits You

凡战必胜，攻必取。不是对国家有利就不行动；
In war, you must win; in attacking, you must take the initiative. If it is not beneficial to the country, do not takeaction;

不能得取胜利，就不用兵；
If you cannot win, do not go to war;

不是处境非常危险，就不作战。
If you are not in danger, do not fight.

国君切不可一时愤怒而动员作战。
The king must not initiate war due to a momentary anger.

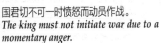

将帅也不可一时怨忿而与敌作战，
Likewise, the general must not attack the enemy with indignation as his basis.

要符合国家的利益才行动，不符合利益即停止。
You must act according to what benefits the country. If it is not beneficial to the country, halt activity.

愤怒可以转为喜悦，怨忿可以转为高兴。

For anger can become happiness, and indignation can become joy.

但是国家亡了，就无法恢复旧观；人死了，更不能再复活。

But once the country is lost, there is no way to bring it back; and once a life is lost, there is no way to revive it.

所以明智的君主一定要慎重用兵，杰出的将领一定要戒惕用兵……

Therefore, an intelligent sovereign will weigh heavily his choice of engaging in war, and an outstanding general will use his forces with caution.

这是安定国家，保全军旅的根本所在。

This is the foundation for maintaining a peaceful country and guaranteeing the integrity of the military.

明智的国君，对于战争遂行的决定，必须绵密考虑，因为它关系到百姓的生死，国家的存亡。

The sovereign must carefully consider any decision to declare war because the lives of the people, as well as the country, hang in the balance.

用间篇
Espionage

用间
Spies

凡动员十万大军，远征千里，人民的损耗加上国家的开支，每天都要用很多钱。

In any war involving 100,000 troops traveling one thousand leagues, the expense inflicted on the people and the country will amount to an enormous number.

而且举国骚动，人马疲于奔命，百姓不能从事本身职业的，将达七十多万家。

In addition, it will cause an upheaval in the country people and horses will be exhausted at the effort expended, and ordinary people will not be able to continue at their normal jobs, totaling upwards of 720,000 people affected.

敌我对抗几年，争的就是最后胜利的一刻……

A war between us and our enemy will be waged for years, only to be finally decided at the last moment...

如果吝啬爵禄和金钱，以致做不好情报工作，不明敌情而遭失败，那就太没有仁心了。

If you do not have good intelligence reports due to stingy salaries and emoluments and you are defeated because of it, that is abject cruelty.

这种人，不是军旅的好统帅，不是国君的好助手，更不能成为胜利的主宰！

This kind of person is not a good commander of troops, is not an aid to his country, and will never become a victorious supreme commander!

所以英明的君主，贤能的将帅，之所以一出兵就能战胜敌人，就是能先了解敌情。
So the reason a bright king and an able general can win victory from the very outset of a war is that they understand the circumstances of the enemy.

要明了敌情，不可取决于鬼神迷信；
To understand the enemy, do not look to spirits or superstition;

不可以用过去相似的事做比较推测；
Do not try to extrapolate from similar events of the past;

也不可以用占卜问卦做依据。
And do not look to divination and oracles.

一定要取决于间谍的情报，才能真正了解敌情。
You must look to the reports of reliable spies before you will understand the circumstances of the enemy.

五间
The
Five
Spies

使用间谍有五种：有乡间、有内间、有反间、有死间、有生间。
There are five kinds of espionage:
village espionage
internal espionage
double espionage
expendable espionage
living espionage

五种间谍同时运用起来，使敌人觉得你莫测高深，有如神话般的奥妙，这是国家元首最重要的法宝。
If these five kinds of espionage are employed, no matter how inscrutable the enemy is, the results will be almost miraculous. This is a country's primary and most important tool.

"乡间"就是利用敌国乡人，做间谍。
"Village espionage" refers to using a villager in the enemy country as one's spy.

"内间"就是利用敌国官吏做间谍。
"Internal espionage" refers to using a minister of the enemy government as a spy.

275

不是才智过人的将帅，不能运用间谍；
Only an extremely clever commander can use spies properly;

不是大仁大义的人，不能差遣间谍；
Only a benevolent and righteous man is able to dispatch spies;

不是用心微细手段巧妙的人，不能鉴别间谍情报之真伪。
Only a man with careful and clever means can tell if a spy's report is true or not.

微妙啊！微妙啊！真是无处不可用间。
Wonderful! Simply wonderful! A spy can be used anywhere.

不过用间的计谋尚未施行就泄露的话，间谍与泄密者，都应处死。
However, if one of our spies is exposed, both the spy and the person who exposed him must die.

更须查出敌方间谍，收买而利用之，作为我方的反间。
Even more importantly, you must find out who the enemy's spies are and try to buy them over to your side.

凡是要攻击目标、占领城塞、刺杀敌将，必须先将其守将、幕僚、秘书、护卫、侍从的姓名、性格都令间谍侦察清楚。
Whether you want to attack a certain place, lay siege to a city, or assassinate an enemy general, you must first have a spy find out the name and character of the commander in charge, his advisors, his secretary, his guards, and his attendants.

借"反间"之助，再培养"乡间""内间"，再借此可利用"死间"假造情报欺敌，再借此而利用"生间"如期回来报告。
Use the help of the double agent to cultivate the assistance of village agents and internal agents. Then, use the expendable agent to fool the enemy, and finally, use the living agent to find out what the enemy's plans are.

所以对"反间"不能不特别优待。
Therefore, you must certainly give very special treatment to the double agent.

这五种间谍之运用，国君应该了解其运用的关键就在"反间"。
In using these five kinds of agents, the king should understand that the key to their success is the double agent.

从前商朝的兴起，是因为伊尹曾在夏朝为臣；
In the past, the reason for the rise of the Shang dynasty was that Yi Yin had been a minister for the preceding Xia dynasty;

周朝的兴起，是因为姜尚曾在商朝为臣。
The reason for the rise of the Zhou dynasty was that Jiang Shang had been a minister for the preceding Shang dynasty.

所以明智的国君和将帅能运用智慧高明的人才作情报工作，一定能成大功。
So we can see that for an intelligent king and general to effectively employ wise and able people as spies will bring certain success.

这是用兵作战的首要，整个军旅都要依靠间谍提供情报，才能采取行动。
This is the initial step of any military campaign. The entire army depends on the information provided through espionage and cannot move without it.

附录 · 延伸阅读
APPENDIX Further reading

此部分为本书图画页的延伸阅读。
各段首所示的页码与图画页对应。

P155 孙子是中国的兵圣，他与古代兵学是分不开的，中国历代讲武论兵，没有不谈《孙子兵法》的，正如明人茅元仪所说："孙子之前的兵学精义，《孙子兵法》中包罗无遗，孙子之后的兵学家，在谈论兵学时都不能超出孙子的范围。"（语见《茅氏武备志》）可见孙子实在是中国承先启后的兵学大师。

P156 照《史记》的说法，孙子是齐国人；照《吴越春秋》的说法，孙子是吴国人，不过两书都指出孙子是春秋时代末期的兵学家，在吴王阖闾三年至十年间，在吴国为将。

P157 《史记》和《吴越春秋》都有孙子操练宫女的记载，不过后世多有所怀疑，宋代的叶适反对最力，他在《习学记言》上特别指出这是"夸大其词，不足采信"。

P158 关于孙子操练宫女的记载，因年代久远，已难考订其真伪，不过《史记》和《吴越春秋》均指陈历历，也不能臆断其非。

P159 司马迁的《史记》和赵晔的《吴越春秋》是记载孙子事迹较为详细的两部书，除此之外，荀子《议兵》篇、韩非子《五蠹》篇、国语《魏语》，都曾提到孙子善用兵，其他有关家世、出身等，则均无记载。

P160 依《吴越春秋》的说法，孙子见吴王阖闾是经由伍子胥的推荐。伍子胥七次力荐，吴王阖闾才任命孙子为将，显见阖闾是经过相当时间观察后，才任命孙子做将帅的。

P161 吴、楚原为世仇，伍子胥本来亦在楚国为官，因避祸而逃至吴，所以伐楚成为阖闾和伍子胥的共同目标，而孙子在受到赏识重用后，成为伐楚的大将。

P162 吴、楚虽为世仇，双方争战近六十年之久，但吴国土地较小，兵力不足，始终无法越过桐柏山、大别山一线，攻入楚国境内。直到阖闾任命孙子为将后，才有了崭新的战略战术观念，长驱直入楚地。

P163 吴王阖闾九年、周敬王十四年，西元前五〇六年，吴军终于攻破楚国国都郢，以一小国的少数兵力而能转战千里，大败楚国这样的一流强国，若非一代兵学大师孙子策划，吴军绝不可能有如此优异的表现，所以司马迁在《史记》上称赞说："西破强楚，入郢，北威齐晋，显名诸侯，孙子与有力焉。"

P164 《始计》是孙子兵法十三篇之首，原来古本兵法没有"始"字，只称"计篇"，后来做注解的人才加上"始"字。

"计"的意思很广泛，在这里至少有三个含义：一是计划、计谋；二是计算、比较；三是预计、分析。其目的就是说明战争前的各项准备工作，特别强调战争之胜负取决于战前的筹划。

P165 由于战争之胜负关系国家之存亡、人民之生死，所以各种比较分析，务必非常慎重。筹划精密，则取胜的公算大；筹划草率，则取胜公算小，如果冒冒失失，毫无计划地兴兵作战，则必难逃失败的命运。

P166 "道、天、地、将、法"，孙子称为"五事"。所谓"道"，主要指政治修明。政治不修而穷兵黩武，则作战必败。"天"则泛指天象、天候等，是作战时必须考虑的条件。"地"是包括地形、地理因素等空间条件。"将"是指统军将帅的能力才识。"法"则是包括纪律、制度、效率等。这五件"事"是作战前，先需要考量的要项。

P167 孙子解释"道"："令民与上同意，可与之生；可与之死，而不畏危也。"这里所应注意的是"令民与上同意"，所谓"同意"，就是人民与政府之间，有共同的信念、目标，要做到这样，必须爱民、亲民，唯有全民竭诚拥护的政府，才能使民众无惧战争的危险，为实现共同的目标而奋战。

P168 春秋时代多迷信，《左传》中记载兵戎之事也有许多卜问吉凶的例子，不过孙子并不是迷信的人，他说："天者，阴阳、寒暑、时制也。"主要是指天候气象之变化，没有任何迷信的色彩。

P169 所谓"地"，系指安营决战之地，亦即主帅对有利的地理形势和空间条件之利用特别重视。孙子在《九变》《行军》《地形》《九地》各篇中，反复说明地形地物之利用要领，足见孙子对于"地利"之取得与否、作为衡量战争胜负的要件，其重视的程度，可以想见。

P170 孙子认为"智、信、仁、勇、严"五者，是为将之道，不过要五者兼备，并不是容易的事，明朝何守法在注解这一段话时说："盖专任智则贼；固守信则愚；惟施仁则懦；纯恃勇则暴；一予严则残。"这里说的"贼、愚、懦、暴、残"，正好是"智、信、仁、勇、严"的反面，为将帅者如行事偏颇，轻则身败名裂，重则丧师辱国，不可不慎。

P171 所谓"法"，就是制度化，军事行动讲求的是效率，要快速灵活，才能收如臂使指之效，这必须在平时就建立良好制度，战时方能发挥力量，所以编制合理、人事上轨道、纪律赏罚严谨、财务军需补给健全，便是克敌制胜的保障。

P172　"七计"：主孰有道？将孰有能？天地孰得？法令孰行？兵众孰强？士卒孰练？赏罚孰明？这七项是知己知彼的功夫，也是对敌我情势的比较分析，其中包括政治、将帅统御、天候地形、士气纪律、训练战力等。

P173　"七计"的工作是将帅在战争前所做的幕僚参谋工作，在各种比较分析中，得出结论，向国君提出建议，所以孙子说："……吾以此知胜负矣，将听吾计，用之必胜，留之；将不听吾计，用之必败，去之。"

P174　孙子列举的"诡道"计十二项："能而示之不能"；"用而示之不用"；"近而示之远"；"远而示之近"；"利而诱之"；"乱而取之"；"实而备之"；"强而避之"；"怒而挠之"；"卑而骄之"；"佚而劳之"；"亲而离之"，都是欺敌、乘敌的方法。

P175　孙子虽然说："兵者，诡道也。"但诡诈计谋并非制胜之唯一要素，为将帅者更不可一味好用诈术，所以孙子先强调"道、天、地、将、法"五事，然后才谈诡道，"五事"是恒久不变的原则，"诡道"只是针对一时一地特殊情况应变的手段，这只要看孙子说"计利以听，乃为之势，以佐其外"便可知其主从、本末了，作战断不能不用"诡道"，但亦不能全依"诡道"，这是孙子强调的原则。

P176　"庙"是指宗庙、祖庙而言，古代出师，必先集于庙堂之上，告祭祖先，以示郑重，同时亦乘此机会集合讨论。所以"庙算"等于今日之最高决策会议，以决定要不要战、能不能战、如何作战。

P177　《作战》篇主要在说明战争对国家和人民所产生的沉重负担，任何一个国家都无法经得起长时期的战争损耗，所以作战愈快取得胜利，愈能减少自身损失而获取战果，因此孙子特别强调："兵贵速，不贵久。"

P178　春秋时代的作战，主要是车战，往往以兵车数量之多寡来衡量一国之实力，此即所谓万乘之君、千乘之国、百乘之家的分别。不过各国编制不尽相同，《大礼》上说，兵车分两类，一是专司攻击之责的，称驰车、攻车或驹车；另一种司运输支援之责的，称重车、守车或革车。司攻击之责的兵车，上乘三人，车左主射；车右持矛；另一人则司驾御马匹，此外再配属步卒七十二人，与兵车协同作战。至于司补给辎重的革车，则配置廿五人，其中炊夫十人、警备五人、厩养五人、杂役五人。所以驰车千乘，计七万五千人；革车千乘，为二万五千人；正好是"带甲十万"。

P179　按周代井田制度，八家为井；四井为邑；四邑为丘；四丘为甸，作战时，每甸出戎马四匹；牛十六头；驹车一乘；重车一辆；甲士步卒一百人；正好符合前述的战斗编组。不过以此推算，每甸计五百十二户人家，需出丁壮一百人，就动员数量来说，相当惊人。不过到春秋末期，井田制度已非原来面貌，军旅动员亦不可能全按这种比例，但无论如何，兴师十万的场面，仍需非常庞大的后勤支援力量的。

P180 战争既然要耗费庞大的人力、物力、财力，所以大军出征作战，以争取胜利为首要，时间拖得愈久，则愈使军队疲惫，锐气尽失；同时长久征战，亦必使国家财政枯竭，所以孙子强调："兵贵胜，不贵久。"

P181 孙子说："役不再籍，粮不三载。"就是仅做一次动员召集，迅速击败敌人，迅速结束战争，不要再做第二次的动员，以免招致民怨。至于粮食之装载输送，也仅两次为限，绝不超过三次，以免国内粮食不足，发生缺粮现象。

P182 古代运粮全仗牛、马车和人力担负，远程运送，受到天候影响、意外损失，以及运送人畜的消耗，到目的地时，大概只剩二十分之一，所以能利用敌人一钟粮食，便可抵得上本国运送二十钟，古代运粮之苦，可以想见。

古制一钟等于六石四斗，一石相当于一百廿斤。

P183 孙子强调"因粮于敌""智将务食于敌"，就是"以战养战"的思想，同时为了鼓励士卒，必须"赏其先得者"，让士卒能争先掠取敌人的物资，以作为自己的战利品，壮大自己的力量。

P184 不过"以战养战"，并非绝对可行，如果敌人实行"坚壁清野"，则"因粮于敌"、"务食于敌"，必成空想，所以用兵必须要迅速机动。在敌人料想不到的时间、地点，乘虚而入，敌人来不及破坏一切，才能享受到胜利的战果，因此孙子在本篇结尾时仍再三强调"兵贵胜，不贵久"。

P185 "谋攻"主要在说明没有战场的战斗行为，战场上杀伐炽烈，不论胜负均会有所损失，因此最理想的方式是不经战斗而取得胜利。想做到这点就必须运用谋略方法和外交手段，达到使敌人屈服的目的，这就是"不战而屈人之兵"，是用兵的最高境界。

P186 用兵的上策是既能取得胜利，又能保全自己实力，因此用谋略的方式；不经血战而能屈服敌人军旅，是最高境界，所以孙子在本篇一开始就提出五个"全"字——全国、全军、全旅、全卒、全伍，就是强调以"全"争天下，也就是希望在不伤丝毫的情况下，取得"全胜"。

P187 孙子说："百战百胜，非善之善者也；不战而屈人之兵，善之善者也。"要想不战而胜，唯有使用政治、外交等手段，造成敌人不得不屈服我的形势，才能达到兵不血刃的目的，这便是"伐谋"与"伐交"。

P188 "伐谋"就是谋略战，运用智谋，订出适切的政略，诱使敌人处处被动，举棋不定，惊惶失措，而使我方能以最小的代价，获得最大的战果。"伐交"则是外交战，系利用外交策略，分化敌人之盟友，联合我方之友邦，使敌人陷于孤立无援境地。战争最高境界，就是使敌人陷于进退两难，不知所措，而我方则乘此良机，予取予求。

P189　孙子最反对的便是硬碰硬的"攻城"，古代攻夺城池，既耗人力、物力，又旷久费时，与"兵贵胜，不贵久"的原则相悖，攻城必经恶战，恶战必有重大伤亡，与"全胜"原则相反，当然是最不宜采取的方式。

P190　古代攻城，伤亡率极高，所以孙子说："杀士卒三分之一，而城不拔者，此攻之灾也。"与"伐谋""伐交""伐兵"来比较，攻城当然是最下策，也是最难奏效的方式。

P191　"伐谋"与"伐交"都是没有战场的战斗，都是利用敌人的心理弱点及现实利害，步步进逼，处处主动，所谓不越樽俎之间，折冲千里之外，造成敌人不得不屈服的形势，这就是孙子所强调的"不战而屈人之兵"。

P192　"伐谋"与"伐交"很难区分其先后层次，不过善"伐谋"者必善于"伐交"；善"伐交"者亦善"伐谋"，两者常交互为用。处处把握以"全争天下"的原则，"兵不顿"（没有重大伤亡）；"利可全"（战果完整），就是"伐谋""伐交"的最高境界。

P193　"伐谋"和"伐交"固然是战争的最高境界，但在实行谋攻战略时，必先具备可胜之战力与必战之决心，否则一味空谈谋略、外交，没有军力和战力做后盾，那就是流于虚张声势了，所以"伐谋""伐交"只是尽量减少伤亡；最后仍然需要依靠武力战斗做最后的解决。

P194　孙子认为我方如在优势兵力情况下，可以"十则围之，五则攻之，倍则分之。"如果在兵力相当或属于劣势时，可以"敌则能战之，少则能守之，不若则能避之"的方式，这是属于野战战法的要领，是用"量"的观念谈作战方法，也就是依敌我兵力的多寡，来决定作战方式。

P195　孙子所列举的野战要领，含有两项基本概念：一是主动；二是弹性。孙子所说的"围之""攻之""分之""战之""守之""避之"，无一不是主动原则和弹性原则的运用，因此绝不能墨守成规，一成不变，必须要把握战机，弹性应变。

P196　将帅统军，负国家之重任，系天下之安危，因此统帅权之完整，非常重要。而古代国君却往往顾忌军权旁落，又恐惧将帅功高震主，怀有二心，所以对统帅权的授予，常有戒惧，所以形成统帅权应否独立的问题。

P197　孙子认为国君侵犯统帅权之后遗症有三：即"縻军""惑军""疑军"，这三种祸患都会干涉军旅的指挥系统，影响战略战术的执行，因此孙子坚决反对国君对统帅权有任何干预或牵制。

P198　孙子说："知胜者有五：知可以战与不可以战者战；识众寡之用者胜；上下同欲者胜；以虞待不虞者胜；将能而君不御者胜。"这五项比较条件，是统帅衡量形势，决定战略战术的运用，与第一篇《始计》中的"庙算"，略有不同，"庙算"是决定国家"大战略"，这里所谓的"知胜"，则是将帅在军事战略或野战战略、战术的考量。

P199 为将帅者，必须有"知彼知己"的能力，孙子特别强调"自知之明"，他认为"不知彼而知己，一胜一负。"也就是说胜负机会各半。如"不知彼"、又"不知己"，必然会"每战必败"，可见孙子对于"知己"的重视程度。

P200 孙子认为对本身战力的培育训练，了解真正实力如何，最为重要，只有在真正认识自我力量究竟有多少的情况下，才能正确判断敌我高下，否则贸然出战，必难逃失败的命运。

P201 《军形》篇主要在说明军事上胜利态势之形成。两军对垒，双方都在找对方的弱点，同时也尽量在隐藏自己的弱点，但自己的弱点并非隐藏就能改变，必须不断地校正改进，才能扭转形势，而改进之道就是在政治、军事、经济、精神各方面，完成充分的准备，以奠定绝对优势的基础，故此在战争准备和战略态势上，应力求万全，应无懈可击之，使敌人找不到我的弱点，而我却能制敌机先，这就是孙子所谓的"胜兵先胜"。

P202 善用兵者，在整体形势上先做到不败的地步，在战争准备与战略布置上求其万全，这就是"先胜部署"。孙子说："先为不可胜，以待敌之可胜。"，这种"不可胜"是操之在我，有赖于万全的准备工作。但是战胜敌人却不是勉强可以办到的，所以孙子说："胜可知，不可为。"就是这个意思。

P203 孙子说："不可胜者，守也；可胜者，攻也。"我不攻击人，自无从取胜，人不攻击我，亦无失败之理，所以说"不可胜"。至于攻击则是主动，集中兵力攻敌弱点，发挥压倒性优势，所以说是"可胜"。但无论攻、守，必先衡量自己的条件，本身条件不足即采守势，有充分条件则采攻势。

P204 无论攻势或守势，都是换取所需要的时间，攻势是在动态中换取所需时间；守势是在静态中换取所需时间。前者是在一定时间内，用积极的行动，捕捉敌人主力而消灭之；后者则是争取时间，延缓敌人行动，伺机决战。孙子形容"攻"与"守"说："善守者，藏于九地之下；善攻者，动于九天之上。"

P205 善用兵者，在整体形势上先要做到不败的要求，即或敌人倾国来犯，我已有充分准备，可以自保，使敌人知难而退。如果敌人在力量上超过我甚多，我也可以使其在"货殚力屈""钝兵挫锐"之余，露出弱点，再逐次扭转战局，这就是"失胜求战"之道。

P206 "胜"与"败"之整体形势，并非开火作战后才形成的，而是在战前就已造成，贸然出兵，战略上已犯了轻敌的毛病，且犯了"不可为而勉强为之"的致命错误，所以善用兵者的"先胜"部署，是胜利成功的最大因素。

P207 孙子举出"度""量""数""称""胜"五个计算程序，以作为预测胜利的要诀。这是对"五事"、"七计"的补充，可以视之为军事战略部署的要领。同时，孙子又再度谈到"修道保法"，以政治修明、法制上轨道，为胜利之基础，可见军事与政治实有不可分的关系。

P208　孙子说："胜兵若以镒称铢；败兵若以铢称镒。"镒是古代的重量单位，一镒为二十四两（一说为二十两），而二十四铢等于一两，所以"铢""镒"之间，相差四五百倍，以此来形容实力相差之悬殊。

P209　《兵势》主要在说明"势"的运用，"势"是力量的表现，如水势、火势，军旅由静止之状态，迅速运动，所形成的威力，就是"兵势"，这一篇与前面的"军形"；后面的"虚实"，有承先启后的连带关系。

P210　兵势首要在作战部置，所以孙子在本篇起首即讲"分数""形名""奇正""虚实"。
　　"分数"是部队编组；"形名"是号令指挥；"奇正"是战法变化；"虚实"是制敌弱点，这些都是兵势部署之要点。
　　进一步说，"分数""形名"是指挥；"奇正""虚实"是战术，正确的指挥配合高明的战术，才能发挥兵旅的威势。

P211　孙子说："凡战者，以正合，以奇胜。"所谓"正"是常道，是不变的原则；所谓"奇"是权谋，是因时地人事而制宜的变化手段。拿《孙子兵法》为例，"五事""七计"是"正"；诡道权变是"奇"。伐谋为"正"，伐兵为"奇"；军形为"正"，兵势为"奇"。奇正相互配合，缺一不可。

P212　孙子说："故善出奇者，无穷如天地，不竭如江河。"所以"正"与"奇"是互变的，正是因为奇变正、正变奇，使人捉摸不定，无从窥知，将帅应运用智慧，做奇正部署，以无穷之变化取胜。

P213　孙子说："声不过五，五声之变，不可胜听也。色不过五，五色之变，不可胜观也。味不过五，五味之变，不可胜尝也。战势不过奇正，奇正之变，不可胜穷也。"就是拿声音、颜色、味觉的变化，证明战势中奇正之变，虽简易实复杂多变。

P214　战场交锋，不但是动作的比赛，而且是力量的较量，譬如猛鸷之扑击，先敛其翼，这就是"形"，一旦动作完成，虚实强弱测定，飞掠而下，一扑中的，这就是"势"的运用，所以将帅随时要注意，把自己的力量发挥到极致，以克敌取胜。

P215　孙子用许多比喻来说明"造势"，如："激水之疾，至于漂石者，势也。""转圆石于千仞之山者，势也。""势如张弩，节如机发。"等，都是在说明"造势"是将帅之责，"善战者，求之于势，不责于人，故能择人任势。"

P216　"形"与"势"实在是一体之两面，一静一动，寓动于静，木石原本是静止的，不去动它，永远不会产生动力，但放置在千仞高山上，滚动而下，运动速度增大，其威力就无法遏止了，所以"势"之运用，全看将帅如何去创造了。

P217 《虚实》篇主要在说明作战贵立于主动地位，避实击虚，取敌人之弱点，而自己则深藏不露，无懈可击。事实上，无论再强大的军旅都会有强有力的部分和较为软弱的部分，这就是"虚实"，善用兵者，一定乘敌之弱，用我之强，以我之强，制敌之弱，此即"致人而不致于人"。

P218 所谓"致人"，是依我的意思支配敌人，我之所欲，敌人虽不情愿，也不得不往；敌人所欲，虽欲往而受我之牵制不能往，这就是孙子所说的："能使敌自至者，利之也；能使敌不得至者，害之也。"

所谓"不致于人"，即处处不受敌之支配，进退自如，避敌之实，击敌之虚，敌不能御，也不能迫我，就是："出其所不趋，趋其所不意。"

P219 "致人而不致于人"含有两个原则，一是主动，一是机动。要支配敌人，必处处主动；要不受制于敌人，必时时机动，以主动配合机动，抢先部署有利地位，诱使敌人进入我所预定的决战地点，或使敌人误认我力量强大，不敢来犯，这就是主动和机动的运用。

P220 "我专敌分"是集中原则的运用，所谓"集中"，乃是在一定时间、空间内，将最大战力放在决胜点上，对敌人实施决定性的打击，以发挥我方之绝对优势。但欲达到此一目的，必先分散敌人力量，也就是让敌人不能集中，故要用佯攻、牵制等等手段，使敌人备多力分，而受制于我。

P221 水本没有一定的形，水因不同之容器而呈现不同的形状，水只有不变的性质而无外在形体，用兵亦复如此，有不变的原则，而无固定方法。以水喻兵，可谓千古名言。

P222 水原本是至柔之物，但是一旦化为激流，则可以滚滚滔滔，有惊人力量，所以水之柔，是水的本性；水之强，是一定的"势"造就成的。水在静态的时候是柔；使之激荡，就转弱为强，所以用兵应注意"兵形像水"的本意。

P223 水一定顺地势向低流，用兵亦必顺应敌情而向其虚弱处进攻，敌之弱即衬托出我之强，这就是乘其弱势而用我之强势。弱和强是由比较得来的，我"专"敌"分"，我才显得强大，所以能掌握形势，善用虚实，自然用兵如神了。

P224 《军争》篇主要在说明会战要领。两军对峙到最后，势必用会战的手段，一决胜负。孙子认为会战最难的就是如何化迂回曲折之远路为直线近路，如何化种种不利的情况为有利情况，因为迂回曲折的作战路线往往是敌人期待性最小、抵抗力最弱的路线，可收出奇制胜之效。

P225 孙子说："军争之难者，以迂为直，以患为利。""迂"与"直"相反；"患"与"利"相背，"直"不可得即以"迂"取之；"利"不可得即以趋"患"之方法诱敌，冀由小害得大利，以迂回方式得机先，所以其中利害关系，必须慎重考量。

P226　会战是大兵团作战，双方都希望在一定的时间内，集结足够的兵力，因此速度成为发挥机动力量的要件。古代道路不良，如人马辎重一齐行动，则速度必迟缓，如弃辎重而急行军，速度虽快，能集结之兵力必相对减少，战斗力亦随之降低；有速度而无力量，如强弩之末，是用兵大忌。

P227　大兵团运动，后勤补给至关重要，如发生问题，后果不堪设想，孙子说："军无辎重则亡；无粮食则亡；无委积则亡。"可见军旅的战力与后勤补给有密切关系，将帅不能只求快速运动，而忽略了后勤的补给能力。

P228　作战区域如在国境之外，则第三国的态变，非常重要，军旅出征，本身接壤之邻国，亦可影响大局，所以孙子注意"豫交"。此外，国境外作战，"地形"及"乡导"亦非常需要了解，如不能善用"地形"和"乡导"，既不能行军，更无法战斗了。

P229　孙子对将帅用兵，举出六个准则："疾如风""徐如林""侵掠如火""不动如山""难知如阴""动如雷霆"。这是说军旅行动要快如"风"；静止时如"林"木无语；进攻时如烈"火"燎原；防守时如"山"岳难撼；隐藏时如"阴"云遮天；快速发动时如迅"雷"不及掩耳。

P230　日本战国时代大将军、也是甲卅兵学之祖的武田信玄最钦服孙子这几句话，他把"疾如风、徐如林、侵掠如火、不动如山"四句话绣在军旗上，作为号志，以后"风林火山"四字就成为武田信玄的代表。

P231　"风、林、火、山、阴、雷"是孙子对军旅作战之要求，如能确实做到，则必定是一支常胜劲旅，不过这必须靠平时不断地严格训练，尤其要具备严整的军纪，才能收如臂使指、号令齐一之效。

P232　《九变》篇主要在说明将帅指挥军旅应注意之事项。将帅为军旅之中枢，负作战成败之重任，因此切不能以一己之好恶，任性行事，应考虑各种状况，做出适当判断，同时用冷静理智的思考方式，以避免错误的决定。

P233　"九变"的解释，历来各家并不一致，大体可分为两种。一是把"九"看成虚数，"九变"即千变万化之意。一是把"九"看做实数，即孙子说的："圮地无舍、衢地合交、绝地无留、围地则谋、死地则战、途有所不由、军有所不击、城有所不攻、地有所不争、君命有所不受。"

P234　孙子特别重视地形，自《军争》《九变》到《行军》《地形》《九地》各篇，都谈到地形地物的利用，而且愈讲愈详细，对每一种地形都从战略及战术方面加以分析，因此本篇中所涉及的五种地形："圮地""衢地""绝地""围地""死地"，在《九地》篇中，都有很详细的说明。

P235　至于"途有所不由，军有所不击，城有所不攻，地有所不争，君命有所不受。"则是五种不同情况下的通变，前四项着眼于战术及战略的考量，至于"君命不受"，乃是强调将帅把握战机，并非事事可以不受君命，"不受命"是为了军旅及国家安全，是一时权变，并不是随便抗命，否则就成为叛逆，绝非孙子所说的良将了。

P236　孙子在本篇中提出"智者之虑，必杂于利害"的观点，即将帅对各种情况之思虑，必居利思危，处害思利，同时将利害两面予以考量，利中必有害，害中必有利，天下无尽善尽美，有利无害的事，要利害互相比较，才能有正确判断。

P237　孙子说："故用兵者，无恃其不来，恃吾有以待之；无恃其不攻，恃吾有所不可攻也。"所以将帅用兵必须要有万全的准备，不要寄望于敌人的失败。

P238　将帅有五项最危险的事：①只知死拼，如暴虎凭河，就可能遭敌人所杀；②贪生怕死，临阵畏怯，就可能遭敌俘虏。

P239　③性子急躁，轻易发怒，就可能受不了凌侮；④廉洁好名，就可能经不起诽谤；⑤慈众爱民，则可能被敌人烦扰。这五项危险，都是将帅易犯的过失，不可不深自警惕。

P240　《行军》篇主要在说明军旅在山地、河川、沼泽、平陆等四种地形的用兵法则，以及三十三种观察敌人虚实的方法。古代交通不便，部队行进的阻碍重重，因此作战时必须因地制宜，充分利用各种地形的特性。同时，大部队运动时，必有一些无法隐藏的迹象，观察这些迹象，便可判断敌人虚实，对敌情研判有极大帮助。

P241　关于"处山之军"（山地作战），孙子主张要"绝山依谷，视生处高"，即靠近山谷前进，同时占据制高点。依山谷进军的好处是谷内的水草可以补充人马体力，占据制高点则是便于鸟瞰敌人，保持警戒，但当敌人已先占高地时，则不要勉强仰攻，须设法迂回。

P242　关于"处水上之军"（河川战），孙子认为部队在渡河之前和渡河之后，其集结位置要与河川保持适当距离，以利兵力之机动。如敌人渡河向我攻击，不要迎击于水中，等其半渡时，其兵力分散在近岸、河中、远岸时，才发动攻击，效果最佳。

P243　关于"处斥泽之军"（沼泽作战），孙子认为这种地形本不宜作战，最好"亟去勿留"，如果一定要作战时，必须靠近水草而且背后有树林依托，因为有树林的地区，土质较密实，不会深陷泥泞。

P244　关于"处平陆之军"（平原作战），孙子认为要选择平坦的地形以利车马，但右翼或侧背要以高地为依托，最好我居高，敌居低，这样使敌人向我攻击不易，而我向敌人俯冲则十分方便。

P245 孙子说："敌近而静者，恃其险也；远而挑战者，欲人之进也；其所居易者，利也。"这是从敌人所居营舍驻地的位置，观察其动静。

P246 孙子说："众树动者，来也。众草多障，疑也。鸟起者，伏也。兽骇者，覆也。尘，高而锐者，车来也。卑而广者，徒来也。"这是从地形地物的环境变化，观察敌人的动静。

P247 孙子说："辞卑而益备者，进也。辞强而进驱者，退也。""轻车先出其侧者，阵也。""无约而请和者，谋也。"这些都是从敌方的行动上观察，以判断其下一步的动作。

P248 《地形》篇主要在说明"通""挂""支""隘""险""远"六种地形的利用，以及将帅因措置失当，以致犯了"走""弛""陷""崩""乱""北"六种错误的情形。

P249 所谓"通形"是平易开阔，四通八达、敌我均可以往来的地形，在这种地形作战，要先占领高地，而且确保补给线的畅通，以便于粮草的输送。

"挂形"是容易进、不易退的地形，如果敌人有备，断我退路，就非常不利。"支形"则是我军与敌军之间有暴露的地段，如湖泊、河川、平原等，谁先出击，谁就暴露身形，所以不可先出，要诱使敌人离开险要，才集中主力攻击。

P250 所谓"隘形"，是指两山夹峙之隘道、隘口，在这种地形作战，应先占隘口，沿隘道做纵深部署，如敌军先占隘口，不要冒险去攻击，但是如敌军守在隘道中间，隘口防守薄弱，则可发动攻击，这就是孙子说的"盈而勿从，不盈而从之"。

P251 "险形"是指山峻谷深，易守难攻的地形。如我军先占，可以逸待劳，如敌人先占，则应放弃正面攻击，另择迂回路线，以免陷于不利地位。

P252 "远形"是指敌我之间相距辽阔，我方没有绝对的优势兵力，又没有有利地形掩护，主动出战，形势不利。所以孙子说："远形者，势均，难以挑战，战而不利。"

P253 "六败"不是地形之害而是人为错误，所以孙子说："凡此六者，非天地之灾，将之过也。"又说："凡此六者，败之道也。将之至任，不可不察也。"主要是提醒将帅要做正确的判断，不要做错误的决定。

P254 不过"六败"之中，"走""北"两项，确属将帅的判断正确与否，其余"弛""陷""崩""乱"四项，都与平素训练、号令纪律有关，所以孙子再三强调："厚而不能使、爱而不能令、乱而不能治，譬若骄子，不可用也。"

P255 孙子在本篇又再度说明将帅之重要性，他认为将帅能"进不求名，退不避罪，惟民是保，而利于至"，这样的将帅才是"国之宝也"。

P256　《九地》篇主要说明九种战略地形："散地""轻地""争地""交地""衢地""重地""圮地""围地""死地"等，以及交战于国境之内和交战于国境之外的用兵原则。《九地》是孙子十三篇中最长的一篇，计一千余字，可以说是对《九变》《行军》《地形》等，有关战场作战地形利用的总结。

P257　孙子说"散地无战"，并非不抵抗之意，而是认为久战于本国之内，士卒思乡顾家，易于离散，所以"无战"是不宜做大规模的会战；而且，大战于国境内，乡里破坏很大，也不是最好的选择。必不得已，非战不可时，亦不必急于决战，可诱敌深入，使敌人力量分散，再伺机决战。所以孙子说的"无战"，实含有多种意义。

P258　至于"争地""交地""衢地"三者，都是属于战略目标，"争地"是兵家必争之地；"交地"是交通要道；"衢地"是枢纽地区，所以皆不能单凭武力夺取，必佐以外交手段，用"伐谋""伐交"的方法取得控制权。

P259　"轻地"是去国不远的地区，士卒畏战思乡的心理，可能仍然存在，所以孙子说"轻地无止"，以免锐气消失。不过就另一方面来看，如果没有深入敌境的打算，亦可轻易退回国境，所以孙子也说："合于利而动，不合于利而止。"

P260　至于"重地""圮地""围地""死地"，都是深入敌境之后的情形。其中孙子最重视"死地"，他除说"死地则战"外，还强调"投之亡地然后存，陷之死地然后生"，以及"死地，吾将示之不活"。这是针对士卒的战场心理而发的，士卒在极端困厄险要的境地中，求生之欲油然而生，自然能发挥勇气，死中求生。

P261　"内线作战"是在中央位置，面对两个或两个以上方向之来敌作战；"外线作战"则是从两个或两个以上方向，向居中央位置的敌人发动攻击。
"内线作战"是在敌人分进而尚未合击时，各个击破；"外线作战"则是由不同方向向目标集中，分进合击，在同一时间内，集中优势力量在一个决战点上，两者之优劣，难以一言蔽之，必须由将帅下决心，做判断。

P262　孙子说："是故始如处女，敌人开户，后如脱兔，敌不及拒。"主要意旨在说明作战必求迅速，在敌人料想不到的时间、地点，发动优势兵力，全面攻击，一举歼灭，这非靠"迅速"不可。

P263　战争是威势与力量的决战，孙子是从这个角度来观察，所以他说："夫霸王之兵，伐大国，则其众不得聚，威加于敌，则其交不得合。"这是政治与军事力量的展示，但毕竟是霸道，而非王道。孙子在十三篇之首的《始计》中，以及其他各篇里，均一再谈到"修道保法"，可见他并不是一个霸道的拥护者，孙子只是就兵论兵，以用兵的威势力量做一总结而已。

P264　"率然"是古代传说中的一种蛇，《神异经》上说："西方山中有蛇，头尾差大，有色五彩，人物触之者，中头则尾至；中尾则头至，名曰率然，会稽常山最多此蛇。"

P265　吴、越是世仇，孙子举吴人和越人同乘一船而遇风浪时，彼此非互相帮助不可的例子，目的在说明士卒在不得已的境地时，非奋战不可的道理。

P266　"九地"之中，孙子最重视"死地"，他除说"死地则战"的话外，还一再强调"投之亡地然后存，陷之死地然后生"，以及"死地，吾将示之以不活"。这些都是针对士卒的心理而发。不过"置之死地而后生"并非用兵常道，不得已而用之，不能以常法视之。

P267　《孙子兵法》中，处处讲"先胜""致人而不致于人"，所以"死地则战"是不得已的办法，"始如处女，敌人开户，后如脱兔，敌不及拒。"使敌人完全料想不到我军行动，才是克敌制胜之道。

P268　《火攻》篇主要说明"以火助攻"的方法，古代作战的防御工事多以木、竹、藤、革等材料为主，易于引火燃烧，因此火攻就是一项有力的武器。如果各方面配合得宜，往往可以一举歼敌，所以孙子专列一章《火攻》，来说明"火力"之运用。

P269　施行火攻必须具备一定的条件，同时引火的工具也要经常准备，时机上要选择天气干燥、久旱不雨的季节。另外还要注意起风的日期，当月亮与二十八宿中箕、壁、翼、轸四宿成一线时，就是起风的日子，所以火攻运用必略知天象不可。

P270　孙子由"火攻"说到用兵是否合于国家利益之大前提，这是颇有感慨之言。因为国君和将帅一怒而兴兵，其后果往往和一场大火后的劫难一样，火焚万户不过顷刻之间的事，而重建恢复，则需极长的时间，因此国君和将帅在兴兵前，必须先考虑是否合于国家利益。

P271　孙子再三强调"安国全军"之道，认为："非利不动，非得不用，非危不战。主不可怒而兴师，将不可愠而致战，合于利而动，不合于利而止。"其基于国家安全的整体考量，真是高瞻远瞩之见。

P272　《用间》是《孙子兵法》最末一篇，《始计》是对战争的通盘考虑估算，所以放在最前面，《用间》是知敌察敌的手段，也是制胜关键，所以放在最后。

　　孙子认为："不知敌之情者，不仁之至也。"是强调情报工作之重要性，如果因不知敌情而失败，则一切努力白费外，还白白牺牲人民的生命财产，所以孙子要批评其为"不仁"了。

P273　《用间》主要说明运用间谍，达到知敌察敌的目的。以举国之力，争胜负于疆场。这是国家人民安危之所系，因此敌人之一举一动都应详为侦察，所以派间谍探敌情实为用兵克敌不可缺少的一环。

P274　《孙子兵法》最可贵的是具备科学的精神，在二千五百年前的时代，孙子能不宥于占卜星象，强调以具体正确的情报工作，作为将帅用兵的研判资料，毫不渗入迷信的色彩，的确难能可贵。

P275 "乡间"和"内间"都是利用敌国的人民或官吏做间谍，孙子说："乡间者，因其乡人而用之；内间者，因其官人而用之。"不过间谍人选的产生，并非易事，而且有时需付出很大的代价才能收买敌国的人民或官吏当间谍。

P276 孙子在"五间"之中，特别重视"反间"，认为"五间之事，主必知之，知之必在于反间"。就现代眼光来看，"反间"之运用之道，也可视之为反情报的工作范围，如"必索敌间之来间我者"。其实就是保密防谍的反制技巧。

P277 孙子说："非圣智不能用间，非仁义不能使间。"间谍深入危境，随时有牺牲之可能，苟无崇高的目标与理想，断不会置生死于度外，人君必行仁义而后才能使间，这是孙子语重心长的话。

P278 间谍所担任的工作是情报的汇集、分析、研判工作，所以举凡军旅所至的地区目标情况，守将习性，甚至其左右人士，门房侍卫都要弄清楚，这种严密的情报资料汇集，当然可以帮助将帅了解敌情。

P279 近代对"情报"二字的定义有"情报即知识""情报即智慧"的说法，可见情报工作非大智之士不能担任，所以孙子说"间必上智""能以上智为间，必成大功"，这是因为整个军旅的行动都靠着情报工作是否正确而后才行动的道理。